animal
coordinating
mechanisms

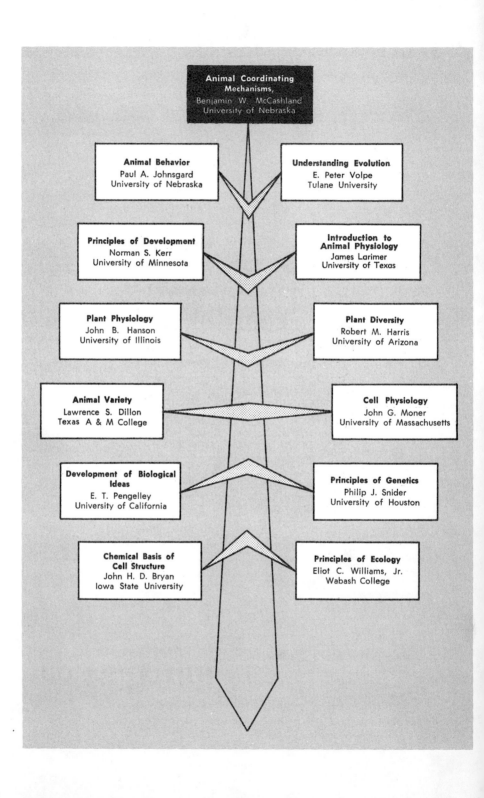

Biology today is in the midst of profound and exciting revelations. This has resulted in a spectacular surge of biological knowledge and the consequent need for new approaches to the teaching of biology. The **Concepts of Biology Series,** designed for the introductory course, transmits the excitement of biology to the college student seeking a liberal education. The underlying theme of each book in the series is to foster an awareness of biology as an imaginative, evolving science. While the individual titles are self-contained, collectively they comprise a modern synthesis of major biological principles.

animal
coordinating
mechanisms

BENJAMIN W. McCASHLAND

Professor of Physiology
University of Nebraska

WM. C. BROWN COMPANY PUBLISHERS

Dubuque, Iowa

Introduction

It is hoped that *Animal Coordinating Mechanisms* will serve a number of purposes, for its preparation has involved more than a singular effort. It has been designed for the student beginning serious considerations of functional biology; he achieved the privilege to make that choice by reason of his earlier classroom experiences. His qualifications are assumed to include some preparation in chemistry and classical zoology and a curiosity to find out why animals behave as they do. It is dedicated to the teacher who feels his obligation to lead those students in a mutual effort to explore basic principles through any and all devices which may be available or need to be improvised. It is written with the hope that it may with that teacher's interpretations stimulate some further interest in his students, giving recognition to one true fact: No knowledge is final and its increase becomes vital as it enables further inquiry.

Coordination and meaningful action is the rule of nature, whether one considers atomic relations, the biochemistry of a cell or the behavior of a larger biological entity. While coordination in the metazoa depends on nervous and hormonal control mechanisms and even the proper relations between these two, we must never lose sight of the importance of looking in both directions: to the molecular level for fundamental reasons and to the general array of animal life for proof of theory through repeated application of those principles. Comparative physiology should include considerations from the realm of the physical sciences through the human domain.

This book is meant to guide thought but not direct it. It is hoped that sufficient fact is furnished to stimulate inquiry, which in turn should lead to the examination of other sources for more detailed accounts according to the interests aroused. It is expected that personal instructional guidance will be furnished in such instances. Few references are given, for it is felt that restrictions should not be imposed on either the teacher or learner for the manner or means through which a course or intellect might be expanded. Free choice should be encouraged in that regard.

Statements on design, dedication and writing of a work, large or small, do not credit the reasons for its being. For myself, I must give credit to those students whose serious inquiry has always been the simultaneous stimulus and reward for gaining and sharing new concepts. Those students give any effort a worthwhile purpose. The mechanics of the task were not accomplished independently. Illustrative materials were made possible through the conscientious efforts of Gregory A. Preston. The final realization of the completed task was possible only through the patience and assistance given by the author's family. For all who have contributed in this effort, either directly or indirectly, an expression of appreciation is extended with the hope of its eventual acceptance.

Contents

CHAPTER 1

The nature of coordination

The need for coordination is present in all living things. Even within the protoplasm of a single cell, there must be an orderly sequence of the various chemical reactions which are accomplished for the cell's maintenance of the living condition. The passage of materials through the membrane—materials that may be sources of energy, waste products of cellular metabolism or ions to be distributed in a particular manner—may be influenced to varying degrees by the action of specific enzymes whose functions must be closely coordinated with that of others. As materials are utilized for the production of energy, enzymes must function in the proper relation to one another so an orderly sequence of events will channel the energy into the appropriate reaction or into another compound within which it may be stored for future use. When the energy is released, a high degree of chemical coordination is again required so that it may be used in a specific way.

Protoplasm, which was once thought of as undifferentiated, is now recognized as consisting of many specific types of structures (organella) which are responsible for the accomplishment of equally specific functions, for instance, respiration, secretion, protein production, self-replication. It is especially important that these structures function in a proper relation to one another. Proof of this is seen in the fact that if cells are disrupted and the various organella merely brought together in a container, the total activity which they display is a fraction of that normally observed, and some functions may be entirely lost.

Within single-celled animals (or acellular animals, as some refer to the protozoa) are seen the beginnings of more complex means of coordination for specialized functions. In the ciliates, where the beat of locomotive organella must be highly coordinated if the protozoan is to move in the proper direction and with the speed required under changing circumstances, highly specialized fibrils beneath the membrane, or pellicle may be involved in this coordination.

As living organisms become larger and consist of an increasing number of cells, there eventually results a division of labor; that is, cells become altered in their appearance and specialized for the performance of particular activities. This is necessary for the benefit of the entire organism. Thus, muscle cells are involved in various types of movement, and glandular cells are concerned with the formation of specific chemical substances, which in many different ways serve the general well-being of the entire organism. But these various types of cells must not be allowed to perform their own particular function without regard to the immediate or changing needs of other cells or of the entire organism.

As one considers the size of an organism and the apparent increase in complexity of its behavioral potentials it should be self-evident that a more complex coordinating system would be required. The total activity of a starfish is less complex than an insect; the frog, if for no reason other than its greater size, is a still more complicated animal. One might follow such a comparison toward still higher forms of life to the primates and man. It is interesting to note, however, that many of the principles of coordinating systems are already established in the so-called lower forms, and these principles are merely further developed or enlarged upon as we follow the progression upward. This has been extremely helpful in many instances, for it has been possible to establish certain facts through study of one form of life and only confirmatory tests are required to demonstrate similar mechanisms existing in other forms. Thus, much information which has been gathered regarding the function of the nerve cell, the main factor in most animal coordination, has come from study of that cell in the squid. In that mollusk the cell is of unusually large size and is especially capable of withstanding some of the conditions to which living material must be subjected in laboratory investigation. Because its cell functions are basically the same as the nerve cells of other animals, it is frequently used in the pursuit of new information which may have application to coordinating function in other forms of life and in a great variety of conditions.

For the most part, coordination activity is accomplished by nerve cells, but all protoplasm is irritable; that is, it will respond to a change in some environmental condition by altering its behavior or function.

Within a single cell there is some means by which information regarding the changing condition is transmitted to its various parts. In some cells there result a number of complex changes at the membrane surface. These changes sweep over the membrane to all portions of the cell, transmitting information of the local change. The long and slender nerve cell has become specialized for the conduction of these surface changes, the total of which have been referred to as the *impulse*. When this impulse is carried to the vicinity of another cell, that cell in turn is informed of a previous change and then excited to alter its function. It is in this manner that messages may be carried into distant regions of the body so behavior of different parts may be altered. Thus, one part of the organism has its functions coordinated with others, and as a rule this occurs to the advantage of all parts concerned. Because of the relative rapidity with which the impulse is conducted over nerve cells and to the various portions of the organism, this type of coordination is quickly effected.

Impulse conduction is not the only means of coordination available in living organisms. In order to alter the behavior of cells in some manner or to perform the function for which they have become most specialized, they may be stimulated by chemical substances in their environment; all cells, as a result of metabolic processes, are continuously producing a great variety of chemical substances. Among these are waste products of metabolism which are generally detrimental to the same and closely adjacent cells. It should be emphasized, however, that not all materials that cells release to their external environment are harmful, for some of these may stimulate other cells in a very particular manner. A *hormone* is a chemical substance produced by one cell which effects a change in the behavior of another cell. As we gain more information on the manner in which hormones function, it appears that they act, along with enzymes, in regulating chemical reactions within the cell. Thus, if the release of hormonal agents is properly controlled, then the entire organism is furnished another means for coordinating the activities of its different parts.

Chemical or hormonal coordination will be effective only as the released materials are able to reach other regions of the body. All cells in an organism are bathed by surrounding fluids, but if simple diffusion is the only means of distribution, then the stimulating effect will be mainly localized, and changes will occur slowly; however, in the larger and more complex animals there is developed a means for circulating body fluids throughout the body. Hormones which are released into the circulating fluids will be more widely distributed with greater rapidity, and the change in behavior will occur in a parallel fashion. In spite of this, hormonal controls are generally effected much more slowly than nervous coordination mechanisms. There is an additional difference in that the nervous impulse will occur and cease with the application of the stimulus so that the resulting body response is also of short duration. A hormone, however, will persist for a longer time and will continue to exert its effect. The period of hormonal influence resulting from an instance of its release may vary from a few seconds to several days. There are particular advantages to nervous and hormonal coordinations, depending on the situation and the type of response required. These will become evident as each is subsequently discussed.

It has already been stated that all cells are irritable; that is, they are subject to stimulation. A *stimulus* may be defined as any alteration in conditions which results in a change in the behavior of a living organism. While spontaneity—the initiation of activity without a stimulating condition—has been considered a criterion for the differentiation between living and nonliving material, this concept is open to question. Man's voluntary and involuntary responses to his changing environment could hardly be called spontaneous since a stimulus has been furnished for such action. In view of the fact that impulses may be directed from one portion of the body to another, and cells in one region may be altered in their behavior by the presence of a hormone which was produced in a distant part, one might question the extent to which actions are completely independent of any external or internal stimulation for their initiation.

At the cellular level one unit may in time alter environmental conditions sufficiently to affect the behavior of its neighbor. Thus, spontaneity would be difficult to identify positively even at that order. Patient observation of isolated animal cells cultured *in vitro,* that is outside the body, will reveal that each cell slowly changes in shape, and this occurs without any evidence that conditions have been altered in the culture solution. Every student in beginning biology has observed amoeboid species under the microscope. Even if extreme care is taken to maintain unchanging conditions in a relatively large volume of water, without mechanical agitation or alteration in illumination and in the complete absence of food organisms which certainly would be expected to stimulate a feeding response, a cell will display protoplasmic streaming and extension and retraction of pseudopodia in an apparently deliberate attempt to move in a particular direction. Surely, it would seem this must represent true spontaneity, for no external change has occurred to furnish a stimulating condition. This does not consider the possibility that internal changes may have accounted for some

4

chain of events which led to increasingly complicated interactions eventually resulting in protoplasmic streaming and pseudopodal extension.

We know that for inorganic chemical reactions only a catalyst is required to set into action a possible combination of reactants with the formation of resultant products. These resultants may in turn become reactants for another catalyzed reaction, producing more and different resultants and so on. Within the cell, enzymes acting as organic catalysts expedite biochemical reactions which may become a part of a long series of changes, each influencing those following through the law of mass action. Excessive accumulation of resultant products, perhaps resulting from several commonly converging reactions, may slow a more sluggish pathway and exert a backward pressure to alter the original balance of progression and even direct chemical reaction into other pathways which were initially less active. Within a cell, organella represent protoplasm specially organized for a particular function, and the activity of one may alter the microenvironment to the extent that another would be called on to increase or decrease its particular function. This would eventually result in changes within the cell and perhaps in its total behavior. As long as reactants and catalytic agents are present there exists the possibility of changing behavior in a living system. Thus, it would appear that true spontaneity is difficult to visualize and that a chemical or physical basis must relate to a stimulus and response.

While all cells contain the potential for general internal stimulation, certain ones become especially sensitive to stimulation by a specific external force. The stimulus in a particular instance might just be light or it might be a particular wave length, an adjacent change in temperature causing the cell's loss or gain of heat energy, a particular chemical in solution or some mechanical force. In the gross functions of our bodies these might eventually be related to our sense of vision, heat or cold, smell or taste, touch or even hearing. In each instance, a specialized cell has responded to its adequate stimulus; that is, the changing condition to which it is especially sensitive. These cells are referred to as *receptors*. They may be a portion of a larger part of the body, for instance, the eye, nasal mucosa, tongue, skin or ear which may assist in directing the adequate stimulus, but it is the receptor cells that are actually responding to that stimulus.

Once the receptor cells are stimulated, they initiate impulses which are conducted along nerves and eventually to a particular portion of the brain. Cells in that area, which receive impulses from only a specific region of the body, interpret them in a particular manner lead-

5

ing to consciousness of changes in our environment. The manner in which conscious interpretation is accomplished is not known, but sufficient understanding exists regarding the processes of stimulation, response and conduction to give them discussion as they relate to animal control mechanisms.

ADDITIONAL READING

MOORE, JOHN A., *Physiological Basis of Behavior*, Garden City, N. Y.: Natural History Press, 1965, pp. 415-477.

CHAPTER 2

The neuron

The membranes of all animal cells possess a characteristic which might make it possible for them to conduct an impulse from one region to another and to excite adjacent cells, providing the proper conditions of proximity existed. Evidence is lacking to indicate that such *general intercellular conduction* is of common occurrence; it is, however, present in the coelenterates, the group which includes the well-known *Hydra*. In the ectodermal region of these organisms are longitudinal musculoepithelial cells which are not only contractile but may as well be conductile, one to another, as a result of their overlapping morphological association (Figure 1). While localized contractions may occur following the application of a point stimulus, even in this animal

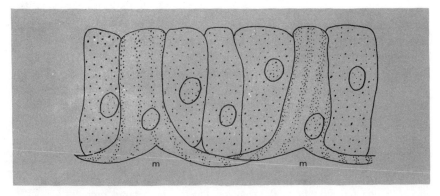

Fig. 1. Musculoepithelial cells (m) in Hydra.

the more widespread contractions are due to the coordinating effect of cells (protoneurons, page 9) more specialized for conductivity.

There is evidence for the existence of coordinating systems even within single cells. Certain of the protozoa display such a degree of specialization in structure and function that it has been proposed that conduction over the general surface would not suffice to explain their complex behavior. These forms represent a logical starting point in consideration of specialized coordinating systems.

THE NEUROMOTOR APPARATUS

Among the protozoa the ciliates show the greatest degree of differentiation; they also display a most remarkable ability for rapid and complex locomotion. *Paramecium* swims forward in a slow or rapid spiral and on striking an object or reaching the vicinity of an un-

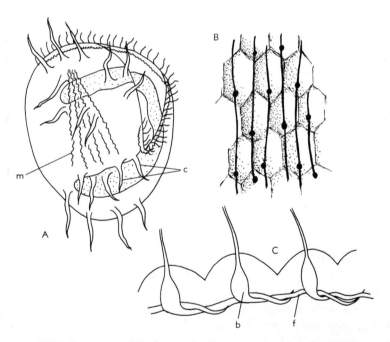

Fig. 2. The neuromotor apparatus: A. Euplotes, showing fibrils (m) extending into areas of cirri (c). B. The silver line system in Paramecium, the hexagonal pattern due to surface indentations. Linear structures are related to cilia. C. Enlarged longitudinal section in pellicle of paramecium showing entwining tapered fibrils (f) extending forward from basal granules of cilia (b).

desirable chemical in solution will suddenly reverse its direction in a strong avoiding reaction. A more specialized hypotrich, *Euplotes,* possesses reduced ciliation and most of the cilia exist as fused tufts, called cirri, on the ventral surface. The coordinated movements of these cirri account for the rapid crawling action which these ciliates display.

Early work by C. V. Taylor, in 1920, stimulated interest in the possible role of the *neuromotor apparatus* in the movements of Euplotes. In the course of investigating the importance of subpellicular fibrils (see Figure 2) in these organisms he noted that there was a loss of coordination of cirrus groups if cuts were made in certain regions of the cell. He attributed this loss of coordination to the sectioning of the fibrils which led to the cirri.

Fibrils of a similar neuromotor apparatus are claimed to exist within Paramecium. In this cell, however, more attention has been directed to structures related to the ciliary rows and lying on or just beneath the pellicle. The patterns are best observed if the cells are treated with silver salts in solution, thus giving rise to the term *silver-line system.* It has been shown that the hexagonal pattern observed actually is due to the deposition of insoluble silver salts in minute crevices on the surface, but the lines that generally follow a longitudinal course are attributed to tapered fibrils extending in an anterior direction from the basal granules of the cilia. These fibrils may establish contact as they intertwine in Paramecium or overlap in other genera. All of these structures should be considered a part of the neuromotor apparatus.

Uncertainties still exist regarding the true role of the neuromotor apparatus in ciliates. If it does function in coordination and therefore in conduction, it represents a system much different from other conducting systems in which conduction is a function of the cellular membrane.

THE PROTONEURON

In higher forms of animal life nervous coordination depends on the function of specialized cells referred to as neurons. These cells may vary extremely in regard to their size and shape, being long and slender or multibranched and of lengths from a few hundred microns to a meter or more. Cells of a much more primitive structure and function are seen in the lowest invertebrates and are referred to as *protoneurons,* the term inferring their more primitive nature. Protoneurons occur as multibranching cells in the ectodermal and gastrodermal regions of Hydra and other coelenterates. Staining with methylene blue reveals these protoneurons form a network throughout the entire organism. At one time it was believed these primitive conductile units actually anastomosed with one another so a sufficiently strong stimulus might result in impulses spreading in all directions, causing the entire organism to contract. More recent evidence indicates that the protoneurons are structurally separate, but the manner in which an impulse may be conducted from one cell to another is probably different from that seen in higher forms of life in which neuron conduction is involved.

THE NEURON

The neuron is the functional conducting cell in the nervous system of higher invertebrates and vertebrates. These cells have their embryonic origin from the ectodermal region, the outermost region of the developing embryo, and during development change in one or more directions, from a spherical shape to elongate eventually becoming either extremely long or possessing shorter multiple branches. The *cell body* controls metabolism of the entire neuron, including its outlying extensions. A single nucleus is present and contains a nucleolus which consists of ribonucleoprotein. The nucleolus is more apparent in the neurons of younger animals and may be completely absent from occasional neurons in older animals. Surrounding the nucleus within the cytoplasm are the *Nissl bodies* which are composed of ribonucleic acid (RNA) and associated with the endoplasmic reticulum. These granular inclusions are more numerous in neurons of healthy animals. It has been reported that unfavorable conditions such as starvation, exhaustion or exposure to certain toxic agents may be followed by decreases in the number of Nissl bodies present. These earlier observations are interesting in view of recent claims that ribonucleic acid may be related to the learning process. Further proof will be required, however, before it may be finally accepted that intelligence and learning are directly related to RNA of nerve tissues. Numerous mitochondria and Golgi bodies are also present in the cell body and apparently function in the same manner as in other cells.

Two types of threadlike extensions from the cell body may be observed: (1) *dendrites*, which are normally shorter and have the function of conducting impulses toward the cell body, (2) an *axon*, which is much longer as a rule and functions in the nervous system to conduct impulses away from the cell body. Nissl bodies are not found beyond the *axon hillock*, the enlarged region where the axon originates from the cell body. This apparently represents a degree of specialization in the neuron, for extensions of protoneurons do contain such RNA

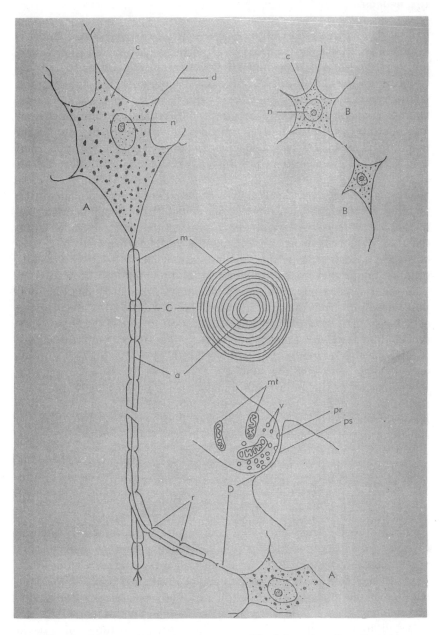

Fig. 3. Neurons (A) and protoneurons (B). Enlarged section through axon (C) and region of synapse (D). Cell body with Nissl bodies (c), nucleus with nucleolus (n), dendrite (d), axon (a), myelin sheath (m), node of Ranvier (r), mitochondria (mt), vesicles (v), presynaptic membrane (pr), postsynaptic membrane (ps).

bodies. That axons and dendrites are dependent on the cell body is evident by the fact that a peripheral portion of a severed neuron will degenerate, although later outward growth from the cell body may account for occasional returns of sensation or movement in a body portion whose nerve supply was previously sectioned. Examination of living neurons through time-lapse photography has revealed a definite streaming of protoplasm in an outward direction and through the axon. This may be the means by which specific materials from the cell body and the nucleus are transported from their site of formation to other regions of the cell.

The entire neuron is limited by a *cell membrane* very similar to that of other cells in the body and composed of lipoprotein material. The membrane possesses permeability characteristics not dissimilar from those of other cells except that it has the particular capacity of instantaneously changing its permeability to certain ions. This property is of primary importance in the conduction of the impulse. The axons of some neurons also possess a *myelin sheath,* a laminated covering composed of alternating layers of lipid and protein material. This structure actually is of a separate cellular origin, formed as *Schwann cells* approach the axon and flatten out as they repeatedly wrap themselves around its circumference. The myelin sheath gives a glistening appearance to that portion of the neuron and accounts for the occurrence of white matter in the brain and spinal cord. On the other hand, gray matter in the nervous system appears as such since a myelin sheath is lacking from the cellular components of that area; it would therefore consist of nerve cell bodies and nonmyelinated fiber extensions. In most myelinated neurons, especially those with axons extending out into peripheral portions of the body, there occur regularly spaced constrictions in the myelin sheath which extend to the axon membrane. These constrictions are the *nodes of Ranvier,* and one theory of impulse conduction places a great importance on their existence.

It has already been stated that neurons are peculiar as cells in their capacity to conduct an impulse, not only along their own length but also to adjacent neurons with which they share a particular association. In a series of several neurons close contact is attained between the axon endings of one and the dendrites or cell body of another. The region of functional interneuron association is the *synapse.* Axon endings are enlarged to form synaptic boutons. Many such structures may be in contact with a cell body and its dendrites, thus the impulses from many neurons may be led to another neuron through these synaptic junctures. Impulses may also be carried from neurons to gland or muscle cells to cause secretion or contraction. These nerve endings may be of more specialized structure, but the purpose of the particular association is still the same: to effect certain processes resulting in transmission of an impulse so the receiving cells perform their particular function.

THE SYNAPSE

The synapse, the region where two neurons come into close proximity and across which an impulse must be transmitted from one neuron to the other, is as important for the functioning of the nervous system as is the neuron itself. Although it might appear that actual contact is acquired, studies with the electron microscope show the existence of a synaptic cleft of approximately 200 Angstrom (20 millimicrons) separating the *presynaptic membrane* of the axon of one neuron from the *postsynaptic membrane* of the dendrite or cell body of the second neuron. If actual contact exists it would be through *transsynaptic filaments* which are claimed to extend from the presynaptic membrane through the postsynaptic membrane and into the cytoplasm of the dendrite. Numerous mitochondria are present in the presynaptic area, indicating a high metabolic activity. Also present in considerable number are *vesicles* of 200 to 250 A. diameter. Some of these appear to discharge through the presynaptic membrane, and it has been proposed that by this means chemical materials may be released to play a role in the transmission of the impulse across the synapse.

The synapse has two characteristics of particular significance: (1) It furnishes a *resistance* to the transmission of the impulse from one neuron to the other, (2) it controls the *direction* of impulse conduction.

The direction of impulse conduction across synapses apparently is established during development. This control allows an impulse to follow a particular course from a receptor to some region of the brain or from the brain outward to cause the contraction of a muscle rather than in the opposite direction. A synaptic nervous system is more typical of higher forms of life. Contrasted against it is the nerve net system of which protoneurons are a part. Since directional control does not exist between adjacent protoneurons (although many structural similarities to the synapse may be seen), a stimulus applied to one region may spread at random throughout the organism. This is especially notable in Hydra, but in some of the higher coelenterates impulses may be transmitted preferentially in one direction. A synaptic system is well in evidence in the higher invertebrates and attains great specialization in vertebrates; however, even in man a nerve net type of structure is present between muscle layers of the digestive system.

The property of synaptic resistance becomes more important and varied in its degree of existence in higher forms of life where size and complexity of behavior requires many more nerve pathways. Even for a single type of response there is a need for gradation, and this may be accomplished in a manner similar to that shown in Figure 4. In areas of greater synaptic resistance, a stronger stimulating force is required, whereas less synaptic resistance will allow the impulse to continue through a multineuron pathway. Thus, a weaker stimulus may result in a weaker or less widespread action, while a stronger stimulus brings forth a more forceful reaction.

Resistance at a synapse is overcome through a process called *facilitation*. Facilitation results from the summation of the effects of stimuli each of which by itself would be incapable of eliciting a response. Facilitation may be either spatial or temporal. Spatial facilitation results when stimuli from many neurons reach a cell body or its dendrites simultaneously so their additive effects result in activation. This type of facilitation is illustrated in Figure 4c where impulses from three neurons are required for excitation. Temporal facilitation results from the arrival of numerous stimuli in rapid sequence so successive stimuli, individually too weak to cause excitation, add their effects before recovery is possible and eventually cause impulse transmission (Figure 4d). From these points it should be obvious that the stimulus must be quantitative both in duration and strength.

The drug strychnine acts to reduce synaptic resistance. In its presence less temporal or spatial facilitation is required for synaptic transmission; therefore, a stimulus normally causing little or no response will now cause an impulse transmission over many opened pathways, resulting in stronger reaction and even convulsive movements. Of course, this type of action would be seen only in animals possessing a synaptic system; the nerve net system, which already has its pathways open for impulses to spread more or less at random, would not be so affected. It must be noted that strychnine lowers synaptic resistance to impulse transmission but does not alter the direction in which the impulse may proceed across a synapse.

MEMBRANE POLARITY

The neuron, like other cells, possesses a membrane of approximately 100 to 120 A. thickness. The membrane is composed of lipoprotein material and is believed to consist of a double layer of vertically oriented lipid molecules covered by an outer protein layer. The protein may account for the wetability of the membrane surface, and there is evi-

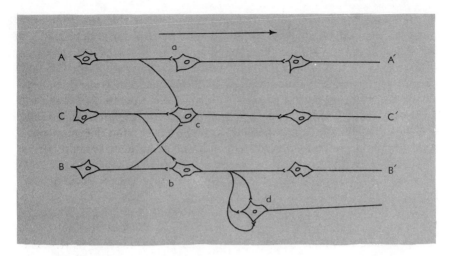

Fig. 4. Interneuron conduction: The impulse passes in the direction of the arrow (A to A' B to B', C to C'). Synaptic resistance is least at a, more at b, most at c, therefore requiring greater spatial facilitation. Temporal facilitation will occur at d.

dence that the lipid content plays a role in the entry or exclusion of some substances, depending on their relative lipid miscibility. It has also been proposed that the membrane possesses pores of approximately 5 to 10 A. diameter. These chemical and structural characteristics of the membrane suggest that permeability depends both on molecular size and solubility. Evidence also indicates that the passage of material inward or outward through the membrane is accomplished with the expenditure of some energy and may involve the action of specific enzymes or enzyme systems. Active processes appear to be of extreme importance for the various conditions and actions of the nerve cell membrane.

The cell membrane also displays electrical properties. This may be illustrated by placing a cell in a solution satisfactory for the maintenance of its structural and functional characteristics, and under the microscope, placing electrodes in the proper position for electrical measurements. One electrode remains in the bathing solution, the other is carefully manipulated to penetrate the membrane with a minimum of injury. If this is properly accomplished a sensitive galvanometer will indicate that the region inside the membrane is negative relative to the outside. Thus, we say that the membrane shows polarity, and we indicate the relative charges, plus and minus, outside and inside, respectively.

All animal cells that have been investigated in this manner show the same qualitative polarity, although quantitative variations may occur. The intensity of this electrical *membrane potential* is generally measured in millivolts and is expressed as –mv, indicating the relative internal negativity. The membrane potential of animal muscle and nerve cells is generally in the range of –70 to –110 mv; animal cells cultured *in vitro* may show values as low as –10 to –30 mv, and protozoan cells have been shown to display potentials in the range of –30 to –100 mv. Most of our information regarding membrane polarity has been gained from studies on the giant axons of the squid, *Loligo*. These neuron ex-

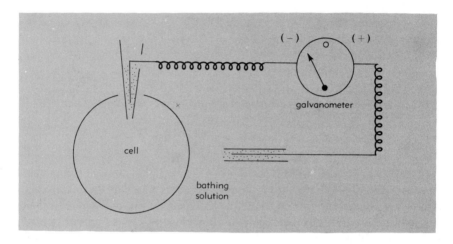

Fig. 5. The nature of the cell membrane polarity.

tensions, several hundred microns in diameter, are isolated and manipulated with relative ease and less danger of damage, which might cause erroneous results. They may be exposed to a variety of external solutions, and it has even been possible to inject them with materials in solution. Protoplasm may also be obtained from these neurons in sufficient quantity for chemical analysis.

A striking observation is made if one examines cells to determine their inorganic ionic composition. If a cellular membrane were to act as a sieve in a purely mechanical manner, one would expect that salts would be at the same concentration inside the cell as they are in the external bathing solution. Such is not the case, however, as the data in Table 1 indicate. Potassium ions are concentrated within the cell, while sodium ions are comparatively excluded. Differences in other ion balances also exist. These differences in intracellular composition are due to the membrane's active role in determining its relative permeability to ions. This unequal distribution of ions contributes to the polarity of the membrane.

The significance of ion disbalances across membranes of particular permeability may best be illustrated with an inanimate model consisting of a container divided by a membrane separating solutions of unequal ionic concentrations. The potential in the system may be measured by immersed electrodes connected to a sensitive galvanometer. In Figure 6A potassium chloride solutions of ten-fold differences in molar con-

TABLE 1

Comparison of ion concentrations on either side of the cell membrane as they occur in the living body.

Ion	Inside (mM)	Outside (mM)
Na	15	150
K	150	5. 5
Cl	9	125

centration are separated by a membrane having a negative surface charge (e.g., cellulose nitrate). In such a situation anions (negatively charged ions) would be repelled and only cations (positively charged ions) would be allowed to penetrate the membrane, which they do in proportion to the difference in ionic concentration and in proportion to the ionic mobility. In such a model the side from which cation diffusion occurs is relatively negative. On the other hand, if the model were constructed with a membrane having a positive surface charge (e.g., a coating of protamine) cations would be repelled and only anions allowed to diffuse with the concentration gradient. In this instance, the side from which the anions diffused would be relatively positive. These examples show that through a cation-permeable membrane a relative negativity arises on the side of higher cation concentration; if anion permeability is present, the side of higher anion concentration is relatively positive.

The nature of the diffusable ion determines the potential of the system, and the quantitative value of the potential depends on the difference in concentration of diffusable ion on either side of the membrane. Thus, a greater potential will be established if a one hundred-fold difference in concentrations exists than if the concentration dif-

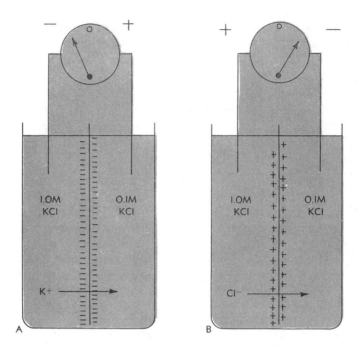

Fig. 6. Development of potentials across permeable membranes: A. The membrane carries a negative charge and is permeable only to cations; B. The membrane carries a positive charge and is permeable to anions. Temporal facilitation will occur at d.

ference across the membrane is only ten fold. The Nernst equation may be used to calculate the potential arising from such a system:

$$E_o = 60 \log \frac{c_1}{c_2}$$

in which E_0 is the potential developed, expressed in millivolts, and c_1 and c_2 represent the higher and lower molar concentrations of the diffusable ion, respectively. Using this formula one would calculate the potential in the model illustrated in Figure 6A as 60 mv.

$$E_o = 60 \log \frac{1.0}{0.1} = 60 \log 10 \text{ or } 60 \times 1 = 60$$

If the membrane in that model had separated KCl solutions of 1.0 and 0.01 M, then the potential would be 120 mv.

$$E_o = 60 \log \frac{1.0}{0.01} = 60 \log 100 \text{ or } 60 \times 2 = 120$$

One needs only remember the rule relating to the direction of cation diffusion to establish the fact that the side containing 1.0 M KCl would be relatively negative in either instance.

The situation seems less simple in living cells and their environment, an example of which was shown in Table 1 (page 17). If the membrane were not selectively permeable then sodium, which is in greater concentration outside the cell, would diffuse inward and cause a relative negativity at the cell's outer surface. Potassium, higher in concentration within the cell, would diffuse outward and give a relative negativity within the cell. If chloride were to diffuse inward from the region of its greater concentration, it would impart a relative positive charge at the outer surface. Actually, the cell membrane in the resting condition is permeable mainly to potassium and not to the other ions which are in unequal distribution. Because of this situation it is possible to assign the relative negativity to the inner surface, and by application of the Nernst equation one would calculate the membrane potential at –90 mv, a value well within the range of experimental findings.

Further proof of the role of potassium in establishing the membrane potential of the resting cell is seen by the addition of increasing amounts of potassium salts to the cell's surrounding environment. As this is done the membrane potential is decreased, as would be expected, in proportion to the concentration gradient. This type of experiment has led to the same results with a wide variety of cells, indicating that potassium gradients are responsible for cell membrane potentials.

The unequal distribution of ions on opposite sides of the membrane could be established only through some mechanism for their movement against a concentration gradient. The term *sodium pump* has been used in reference to the reactions for moving sodium out of the cell, and a similar system might well be involved for the internal concentration of potassium. Whatever materials might be involved in a pumping mechanism, it is apparent that energy would be required. Evidence indicates that adenosine triphosphate (ATP) serves as the energy source for ion movement. If nerve cells are treated with agents which prevent the formation of ATP and are then stimulated so that an increase in energy expenditure results, the resting membrane potential gradually diminishes. Limited success has been attained in restoring that potential by the injection into the cell of ATP solutions.

In order that ATP may be formed other substances in the cell must be used to furnish the energy. This energy may be derived to some extent from carbohydrates. It is also thought that neurons may derive much of their energy through amino acid and protein catabolism. Evidently, aerobic oxidative processes are not of immediate necessity, for a neuron in the absence of oxygen will continue its normal function for long periods of time. When oxygen is eventually restored, however, there is a brief period of accelerated utilization, indicating the capacity for the cell to enter a condition of oxygen debt. From this it would appear that the oxidative processes in nerve tissue which are involved in energy production are not unlike those active in other tissues.

CHAPTER 3

The conducting neuron

Since irritability is a property of all protoplasm, it follows that living material will respond to a change in its environment by changing the degree or nature of its activity. In order to study the changes in behavior of living material an appropriate stimulus must be applied in the proper manner. For that reason, an appreciation of the types and characteristics of stimulating conditions is essential.

METHODS OF STIMULATION

There are five means of stimulation which may be effective. These will be considered briefly, especially with reference to their proper employment.

Mechanical stimulation may be applied to amoeba or voticella to cause avoiding reactions. If a nerve, with its connected muscle intact, is struck with a blunt instrument, the muscle will contract. This indicates that the nerve was stimulated and caused to conduct an excitatory impulse to the muscle. Stimuli of this sort are injurious to the tissue, so effective use of mechanical stimulation is limited mainly to the gentle application of pressure in studying receptors for touch and pressure. Some receptors in muscles are stimulated by stretching, another example of mechanical stimulation.

Thermal stimulation involves the application of heat or cold. In either instance, heat energy is the actual stimulus, cold being a negative quality resulting from the loss of heat. Application of a heated wire may stimulate a nerve or muscle, but damage will result. Thermal stimulation is best used in the study of those receptors in the skin concerned especially with sensations of heat and cold.

Photostimulation, within the range of the visible spectrum, is effective on visual or photoreceptors. Shorter or longer wave lengths, in order to be effective on other types of tissues, have to be applied with such intensity that they may be damaging.

Chemical stimulation may be desirable depending on its employment. The application of salt crystals to muscle or nerve will result in stimulation, but damage to the tissues is likely. On the other hand, the application of chemicals normally associated with stimulation changes in the tissues may be a desirable means of stimulation since it closely approximates the normal situation. Chemical stimulation is the normal means of activating receptors for taste or smell. Hormones are chemicals produced within the body which cause changes in function of body parts. It should be noted that chemical stimulants must be dissolved in order to be effective.

Electrical stimulation is most frequently used for experimental purposes since it approaches the normal stimulating condition, is easily applied and its intensity and the duration of its action is controllable. Electrical stimulation is the method of choice for nerve and for muscle study and may also be employed quite appropriately for receptors which might normally be stimulated by some other means.

ESSENTIAL QUALITIES OF THE STIMULUS

The proper choice of stimulus is not the only consideration. In order that a stimulus may be effective, three of its attributes must be considered and properly controlled. They are as follows:

1. The *intensity* of the stimulus relates to the extent of actual change in condition. Obviously, a stimulus that is too weak would not cause a response. A *minimal stimulus* is the one of least intensity which will cause a response. In some instances, increasing the intensity will cause, within limitations, stronger measurable activity. That intensity above which no further increase in response is noted is referred to as the *maximal stimulus*. Supramaximal stimuli of too great intensity might be injurious and should be avoided.
2. The *rate of change* is important for proper effect. The stimulus is most effective if its full intensity is quickly obtained. A very considerable change, if achieved slowly, may not cause any response at all; on the other hand, a less intense stimulus involving rapid change may be quite effective.

3. The *duration of the stimulus* is the period of time during which the change in condition is caused to act. Although important in electrical stimulation, it is more easily visualized in employment of stimuli of other types. The application of pressure or temperature changes may be effective only if they are of sufficient intensity, applied in such a way to cause a rapid change and act through a minimum of time. This implies that the stimulus must cause a certain quantity of change within the living material in order to be effective. The *latent period* is the time elapsing from the initial application of the stimulus until a detectable response occurs.

The importance of these considerations in stimulation is seen in the strength-duration curve. In the hypothetical situation shown in Figure 7, it is apparent that as the intensity of the stimulus is increased (it being assumed that the rate of change remains constant) the time during which it must be applied in order to produce a response diminishes. Furthermore, there is an intensity below which no response will occur regardless of its duration. This is the *rheobase* intensity. For experimental purposes the rheobase is doubled and the reaction time, or *chronaxie* is noted. By comparison of chronaxie values one gains an appreciation

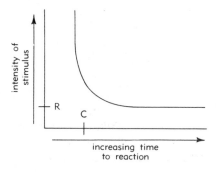

Fig. 7. Hypothetical strength: duration curve. Rheobase (R), chronaxie (C).

of the relative reactivity of tissues. Chronaxie is less for nerve than for skeletal muscle (the type of muscle responsible for body movements), and smooth muscle from the stomach or intestine has a still greater chronaxie value. This illustrates the rapid response of neurons to a stimulating condition and indicates their suitability for coordinating action.

MEMBRANE CHANGES IN STIMULATION

If a stimulus is applied near one of two sensing electrodes, placed some distance apart but in contact with the surface of a neuron, it may be demonstrated that a relative negativity arises near the point of stimulation. If one of a pair of electrodes attached to a galvanometer is caused to penetrate the membrane it will be seen that there is an immediate loss of membrane polarity following stimulation; as a matter of fact, the membrane will show a slight reversal of its polarity before returning to normal. The change may be studied using the cathode ray oscilloscope, and the recorded changes, which may be completed in as little as 0.0015 second, are indicated graphically in Figure 8.

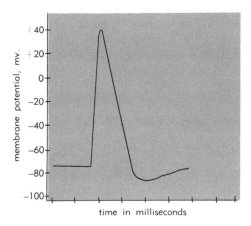

Fig. 8. Polarity changes of the neuron membrane on stimulation.

The change in the membrane polarity is due to changes in its permeability. It has been established that the resting potential results from the diffusion of potassium at higher concentration within the cell, outward through the membrane. Stimulation causes an altered membrane permeability so that sodium ions, at a higher concentration outside the cell, are allowed to move inward at a high rate. This inward cation movement first offsets the effect of outward potassium diffusion so that a relative negativity is no longer associated with the inner membrane surface and by its continuation results in a negative charge at the outer surface. This slight reversal of the potential is recorded as the *overshoot*. The disruption of the normal membrane condition persists for but a brief time, and as sodium permeability diminishes outward diffusion of potassium briefly surpasses normal, hastening the return toward the resting potential and even causing a slight hyperpolarization to exist temporarily. One must keep in mind that these changes occur with extreme rapidity.

The polarized condition is essential in order that a stimulating condition may be effective, and while the membrane is depolarized another stimulus is without effect. The neuron is then refractory, but as soon as polarity is restored the refractory period is ended and the neuron may again respond to stimulation. The amount of ionic movement for the maintenance of polarity and depolarization is extremely small, and since the membrane continues to concentrate potassium inside the cell and to extrude sodium, repeated stimulation may occur for long periods of time with relatively little change in the ionic balance.

In the preceding paragraphs, we have considered the effect of the stimulus in the immediate region of its application. Actually, the effect is not limited to that point, and this may be shown by another experiment. Two electrodes are placed in contact with the neuron surface and at some distance apart, as indicated in Figure 9. Electrical changes

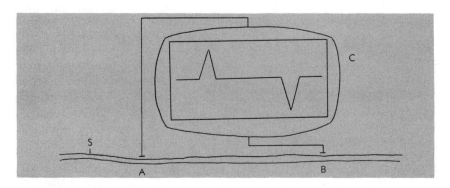

Fig. 9. The action current in a neuron: point of stimulation (S), electrodes placed in contact with the neuron surface (A, B), and connected to a cathode ray oscillograph (C).

at the membrane surface are indicated on the oscilloscope screen. Following stimulation of the neuron at a point beyond either of the electrodes, the electron beam, as it traces across the screen, will be observed to move in the direction of the electrode nearer the point of stimulation, return to its base line and then deflect momentarily toward the electrode more distant from the point of stimulation. The deflections, or *spike potentials* are similar to that seen at the point of stimulation and are properly interpreted as being due to temporary depolarization. The stimulus has not only resulted in depolarization at its point of application, but the change has swept rapidly along the length of the neuron, with repolarization occurring immediately thereafter. This sweeping

25

electrical change is called the *action potential* and is an indication of the impulse passage. Actually, the impulse travels from its origin in both directions along the length of the neuron, but in a series of several neurons within the body it will be allowed to continue from one neuron to another in only one direction, that being determined by the synapse.

The rate at which the impulse travels and the height of the spike itself are functions of the neuron rather than the stimulus. The rate of conduction varies directly with the diameter of the fiber (neuron) and the thickness of the myelin sheath. Nonmyelinated fibers conduct quite slowly. Mammalian nerve fibers have been placed into three groups according to their diameter and rate of conduction. Type A fibers are heavily myelinated and conduct impulses at rates from 5 to 120 meters per second. In the body these fibers initiate voluntary movements and carry impulses concerned with conscious sensations. Lightly myelinated fibers carry impulses at rates of 3 to 15 meters per second, and small nonmyelinated fibers conduct impulses concerned mainly with involuntary control of internal organs at rates of about 0.5 to 2 meters per second. That conduction is a function of the membrane may be shown by cooling a portion of the neuron or exposing it to narcotic agents. The impulse will travel at the usual rate along the normal portion of the fiber, will proceed slowly through the effected region, then return to its normal rate after having passed that area.

The changes in polarity and permeability are summarized in Figure 10. Immediately following stimulation the membrane undergoes slight depolarization. During that very brief *period of latent addition* the neuron displays increased excitability. If the change is insufficient; that is, if the stimulus is subminimal, the membrane returns to its normal resting state. However, a sufficiently strong stimulus or several weaker stimuli applied in very rapid succession will result in depolarization to the extent that the spike potential will develop and progress along the neuron.

With the changes that occur accompanying the spike the neuron is in such a condition that it could not respond to a second stimulation; this is the *refractory period*. The refractory period in neurons may range from 0.0005 to 0.002 second. Its duration varies inversely with the speed of conduction. It follows, then, that the more rapidly conducting neurons would be capable of conducting many more impulses per unit time than could those that conduct more slowly.

For a brief period following the spike potential, potassium diffuses outward at a more rapid rate. This aids in the membrane's return to the normal state as impermeability to sodium ions is restored. These

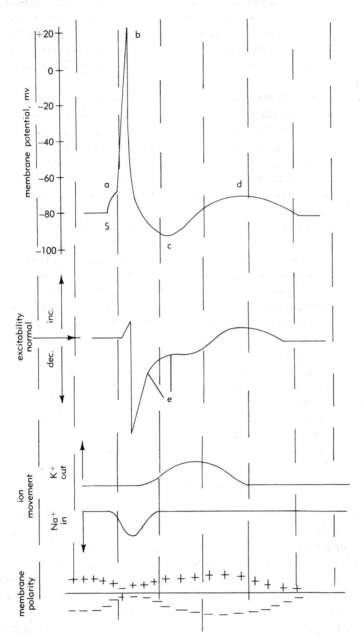

Fig. 10. Events during the spike potential: stimulus applied (S), period of increased sensitivity (a), spike (b), negative after potential (c), positive after potential (d), refractory period (e).

27

changes may actually cause a hyperpolarization during the period of the *negative after potential.* There may also be seen a *positive after potential,* a period during which a residual partial depolarization persists and excitability is slightly increased.

This examination of the spike indicates that brief changes from the normal potential will relate to the excitation process, and shifts in permeability will make it more or less probable that a second spike potential may develop as a result of a second and closely following stimulation. These factors are especially important in considering the transmission of the impulse across a synapse.

The type of conduction which has been considered assumes that the impulse progresses at a constant rate over the length of the neuron. This may be the situation in the nonmyelinated fiber, but in myelinated neurons conduction may be *saltatory,* progressing from one node of Ranvier to the next in a stepwise fashion. It has been shown that excitability is much greater at the nodes, where the myelin sheath does not furnish insulation and a barrier to ionic movement. The internodal distance is greater in thickly myelinated neurons, and it has been proposed that this is related to the more rapid rate of conduction in these fibers. Even in saltatory conduction the same ionic and chemical factors may be involved as those given in this general discussion.

It is highly probable that chemical materials are involved in the normal condition of the membrane and that reactions involving them relate to changing permeability during depolarization. One of the materials frequently mentioned in this regard is *acetylcholine* (ACh), which may be formed or broken down in nerve tissue according to the reaction:

$$\underset{\text{choline}}{\underset{|}{CH_3}\atop CH_3-N-CH_2-CH_2-OH \atop \underset{|}{CH_3}} + \underset{\text{acetic acid}}{HO-\underset{\underset{O}{\|}}{C}-CH_3} \underset{\text{cholinesterase}}{\overset{\text{choline acetylase}}{\rightleftarrows}} \underset{\text{acetylcholine}}{\underset{|}{CH_3}\atop CH_3-N-CH_2-CH_2-O-\underset{\underset{O}{\|}}{C}-CH_3 \atop \underset{|}{CH_3}} + H_2O$$

Acetylcholine is present in the brain and in nerve fibers lying outside the brain and spinal cord. It appears during embryonic development at about the same time electrical activity in nervous structures is first detected. An objection to the theory that ACh might be involved in neuron conduction is based on the observation that its application to nerve tissue may not result in impulse transmission or even slight depolarization. One must recall, however, that the lipid nature of the membrane and surrounding myelin sheath would act as a barrier to the penetration of water soluble ACh applied at the surface. If lipid-miscible materials closely related to ACh in certain aspects of their molecular structure are applied to the neuron, a prolonged depolarization results. Furthermore, that region so treated is not capable of excitation or conductivity and seems to persist in a refractory state. This sort of evidence strengthens the theory that ACh may be involved in impulse conduction.

Most of the ACh present in nerve tissue exists in close association with protein material and is referred to as "bound ACh." This form would be no more active than would that which is topically applied, since it would not be available for chemical reactions within the membrane. When a nerve structure is stimulated there is a transitory increase in free ACh, apparently as a result of its release from the bound form. The free ACh disappears quickly as it is destroyed by cholinesterase. This destruction is essential; if the theory is correct that ACh is responsible for depolarization, its persistence would result in a continued refractory state, while actually the neuron may conduct many impulses per second.

Many studies have indicated that the action of ACh is highly dependent on its structure. If the molecule is changed slightly there is a marked decrease in its activity. This observation is in good agreement with the theory that cholinesterase has particular chemical groups at its surface with which ACh must match. It is proposed that stimulation releases ACh which then reacts with cholinesterase and that as this occurs the enzyme changes its configuration (Figure 11). The change in shape of cholinesterase results in a change of membrane structural organization and permeability. With that condition sodium ions are allowed to diffuse inward, and the spike potential arises. Since enzymatic reactions occur with extreme rapidity (it has been estimated that the equivalent of one square millimeter of neuronal surface has sufficient cholinesterase to split 1×10^9 molecules of ACh in 0.001 second), the combination of enzyme and substrate exists briefly before the ACh is split into its component parts. The enzyme is then allowed to return to its original configuration, and the membrane returns to its normal resting condition. It only remains that the choline and acetic acid be recombined by the action of choline acetylase, with the expenditure of energy available from ATP, and the ACh so formed be bound by protein until another stimulus causes the cycle to be repeated.

While direct proof for this theory is lacking, the presence of free and bound ACh and the two enzymes in nerve tissue encourages its consideration. The structural characteristics determining membrane permeability and the mechanisms which might be involved in ion segrega-

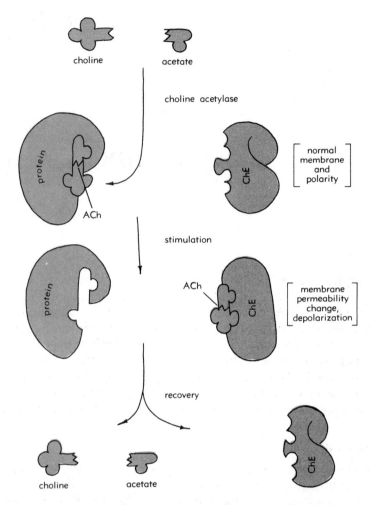

Fig. 11. Hypothetical scheme for acetylcholine (ACh) and choline-sterase (ChE) involvement in the neuron membrane during excitation.

tion across the membrane—the so-called sodium pump—are still very much in question.

ADDITIONAL READING

SCHEER, BRADLEY T., *Animal Physiology*, New York: John Wiley & Sons, Inc., 1963, pp. 87-103.

CHAPTER 4

Synaptic conduction

It has been stated that an impulse may be transmitted in only one direction across a synapse. The same is true for conduction from nerve to muscle or from a receptor cell to a nerve. This is evident because a severed neuron may eventually grow outward to the original region of its endings but will establish a functional association only with muscle or receptor according to its original action. These peculiarities of neural relations are related to specific electrical and chemical reactions occurring at the synapse. In this discussion we shall also consider impulse transmission from nerve to muscle or glandular tissue.

SYNAPTIC POTENTIALS

The spike potential passes along the length of the axon at constant intensity until it reaches the presynaptic region. At that point it diminishes and excitation across the synapse will depend on a number of events in that area. Careful analyses of potentials in the postsynaptic region also indicate that a spike potential does not immediately arise at that point. Instead, the resting potential is altered slightly in the direction of depolarization in the instance of excitation or toward hyperpolarization for inhibition.

The postsynaptic change of most importance is the one preceding the development of a spike potential and is referred to as the *excitatory postsynaptic potential* (EPSP).

The electrical and chemical processes (page 33) occurring at the synapse cause changes in the postsynaptic membrane to allow for depolarization. A single EPSP may be related to such a slight depolarization that the spike potential will not develop and be self-propagating; the slight depolarization is of very brief duration and the potential returns to the normal condition. If, however, a rapid series of such changes occur, each EPSP will be superimposed upon the previous one. This results in an additive change which may eventually become sufficiently great to allow the spike to appear and continue along the neuron. The situation shown in Figure 12A represents events as they might occur in temporal facilitation. It is also possible that multi-synaptic associations in an area might by nearly spontaneous activity effect spatial summation through the additive effects of the individual EPSP's.

In some instances, inhibition rather than stimulation may be the net effect at the synaptic region. The results are seen when one presses against the upper lip to suppress a sneeze. Another example is seen in rhythmic breathing movements. As certain muscles contract under nervous stimulation the chest expands. This effects a stretching of the lungs and furnishes mechanical stimulation to receptors. There follows a transmission of impulses to an appropriate region of the brain to inhibit the activity of those nerves which first caused inhalation. With the discontinuation of muscular stimulation the chest recoils to its original condition so that receptors are no longer stimulated by stretch, and the inhibitory impulses are discontinued. Thus, nerves again are free to transmit impulses to muscles, causing inhalation. The process is then repeated.

Inhibitory actions also occur at synapses within the spinal cord, and it is through studies of this region that evidence has been gained on the nature of synaptic conditions during inhibition. Properly placed electrodes reveal the occurrence of *inhibitory postsynaptic potentials* (IPSP) which are similar to the EPSP except they represent a transitory hyperpolarization (Figure 12B). Their effects may also be additive. With hyperpolarization occurring in the synaptic region it is less likely that an excitatory stimulus may be effective in causing the development of a spike potential. Inhibitory effects at the synapse may last longer, thus making the resistance more difficult to overcome.

The occurrence of postsynaptic potentials is related to membrane permeability. Changes in the EPSP are suggestive of the beginning of the spike and inward sodium passage. It has been shown that during the IPSP there is an increased permeability to potassium and other smaller ions, while the slightly larger sodium ion is not allowed to diffuse inward. This condition would lead to hyperpolarization.

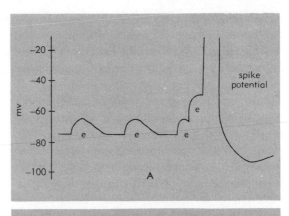

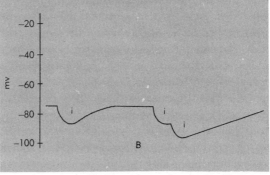

Fig. 12. Membrane potential changes related to synaptic transmission: A. Depolarization of the EPSP (e) and spike development through temporal summation; B. Hyperpolarization of the IPSP (i).

In addition to the electrical changes which have been recorded from the synaptic region, there are visual and chemical evidences for the occurrence of particular events. The electron microscope has shown the presence of vesicles in the presynaptic area (Figure 3). It has been postulated that these vesicles are the means by which chemical substances may be released into the synaptic cleft and that their particular presence is the cause for transmission of the excitation. Miniature potentials may be recorded from synaptic regions, and it has been proposed that these result from random vesicular discharge. An excitation would depend on the simultaneous release of a larger quantity of material from many vesicles.

CHEMICAL ACTIVITY IN SYNAPTIC TRANSMISSION

The involvement of chemical agents in synaptic transmission was recognized before theories were advanced attempting to relate ACh to neuron transmission. Before the turn of the century it was shown that stimulation of the vagus nerve, which leads from the brain to many visceral or internal organs including the heart, would cause that organ to slow or temporarily cease its automatic rhythmic contractions. Shortly thereafter, it was observed that the application of ACh solutions caused the same slowing as did vagal stimulation. In 1921 the German physiologist Otto Loewi performed an experiment to demonstrate the involvement of chemical substances in nervous control of the heart. Two frog hearts, which continued to beat for a time following their removal from the body, were arranged so that a salts solution flowed through the vessels into and through the first and then into the second heart. When the vagus nerve of the first heart was stimulated the heart was inhibited in its beating, and a short time later the second heart was also inhibited, although its vagus nerve had not been stimulated. Loewi concluded from that experiment that a chemical material was released from the vagus endings of the first heart and caused inhibition there as well as in the second heart as it was carried forward. It was later demonstrated that ACh was the agent responsible for mediation of the vagal effect. These observations have been extended to many other nerves which because of this means of chemical impulse mediation are referred to as *cholinergic*.

It has also been shown that ACh is responsible for transmission of impulses from nerve to many visceral muscular structures, inhibiting contraction of sphincters (heavy muscle rings) between the stomach and intestine and at the base of the urinary bladder and stimulating contraction of the walls of the stomach and intestine and muscles in the air passageways in the lungs. Secretion of the salivary glands and contraction of the pupil of the eye are other examples of actions caused by cholinergic nerves. The release of ACh is related to the transmission of a stimulus from nerve to skeletal muscles, causing voluntary body movements. It is also responsible for the conduction of impulses across synapses in many regions of the nervous system. This action includes the brain, but its importance in transmission within the spinal cord is less firmly established.

Wherever ACh is produced, cholinesterase is also found. The possible relation of the enzyme to changes in membrane permeability during excitation has been discussed. Its value is also seen in its rapid destruction of ACh so the effect is not prolonged beyond the period of nerve action. Loewi's success in transfusing ACh from one heart to another is due to the use of a salts solution for perfusion. Blood contains cholinesterase which would destroy the material before it could reach and affect the second heart. Some drugs, such as eserine and diisopropyl fluorophosphate (DFP) prevent the action of cholinesterase with the result that ACh is allowed to accumulate. The application of these materials will result in a great accentuation of the effect of cholinergic nerve stimulation. They are used experimentally in studies on suspected cholinergic structures which may produce so little ACh that its effect is not normally seen prior to destruction.

ACh may be involved in impulse transmission in lower forms of life, since both it and cholinesterase have been detected in nervous tissue of arthropods and mollusks. The fact that relatively high concentrations of ACh solutions must be applied to nervous tissues in these forms in order to cause detectable impulse transmission may be due to the failure of the chemical to penetrate cellular structures. Cholinergic nerves lead to the musculature and intestine of annelids. It is doubtful that ACh is involved in neural transmission in the flatworms, and evidence indicates its absence in coordination within coelenterates and sponges. ACh has been reported in some of the protozoa, and there is evidence for the presence of cholinesterase in the pellicular region of ciliates. It is interesting to speculate on its role in coordination of ciliary movement through associations of interciliary fibrils (Figure 2), but much more work remains to be done before definite conclusions may be drawn. It appears that while ACh is of particular significance in nervous activity of the vertebrates, other materials play such a role in the invertebrates.

In addition to ACh, *epinephrine* and *norepinephrine* are involved in neuromuscular transmission in the vertebrates:

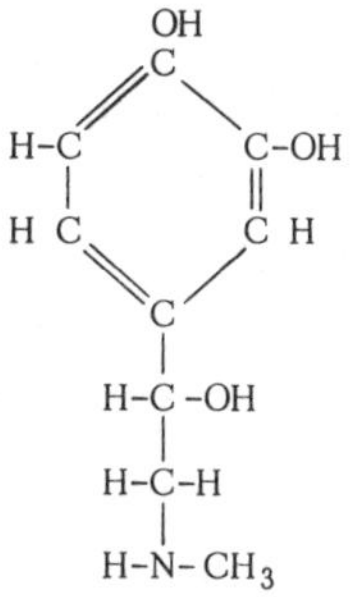

epinephrine

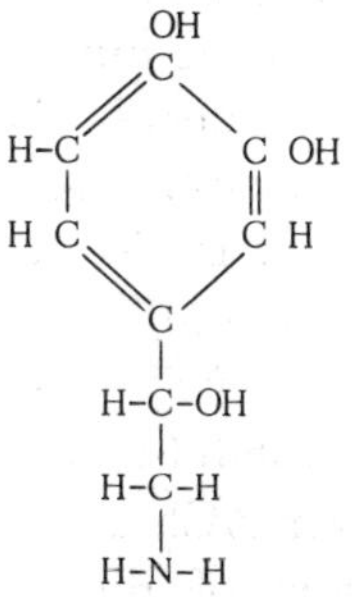

norepinephrine

These materials are released from the endings of neurons, causing the heart to beat faster; others lead to visceral organs, generally having an action just the opposite of the cholinergic nerves. Neurons, the actions of which are due to the release of epinephrine or norepinephrine, are

35

referred to as *adrenergic*. Prolonged action of epinephrine is prevented by its oxidation, but this destruction occurs much more slowly than does ACh by cholinesterase. Although adrenergic structures are probably more limited to vertebrates, there is indication of their occasional occurrence in certain mollusks and crustaceans. Materials have been extracted from some insects, worms and even paramecium which when applied to sensitive mammalism tissues, have an epinephrine-like action; however, their chemical structure has not been proven. Epinephrine and norepinephrine are also produced by the adrenal gland and released into the blood stream. Upon reaching the proper muscular and glandular structures the materials may cause the same types of action observed after nervous stimulation. The significance of epinephrine as an endocrine substance will be considered in Chapter 10.

Other materials have been identified in a variety of transmissions. In the brain, *serotonin* (5-hydroxytryptamine, 5HT) is involved in nerve metabolism and may be related to conduction. *Gamma aminobutyric* acid is apparently involved in transmission in crustaceans and is claimed to be extractable from certain portions of the vertebrate spinal cord. *Tyramine* enhances transmission in certain of the anemones and may be involved in nerve net activity. Other substances as simple as ATP and as complex as unidentified polypeptides have been claimed to be involved in nerve activity. The status of most of these substances awaits further clarification.

It has been noted that neural transmitting agents may be stimulatory in some instances and inhibitory in others. The exact reason for this difference in action is not known, but interesting theories have been presented in an attempt to explain the dual action. About thirty years ago W. B. Cannon of Harvard University, while studying the action of adrenergic structures, proposed that the chemical transmitter was produced in one of two different forms, *sympathin E* (excitatory) and *sympathin* I (inhibitory). The agent was so named because he was working with nerves of the sympathetic nervous system, which controls many involuntary actions of visceral organs. The actions of epinephrine and norepinephrine have been compared and found similar to those of sympathin I and E, respectively. In recent thought the sympathin theory is mainly of historical interest.

Evidence gained from studies on ACh and cholinergic structures indicates that the chemical mediator is always the same but that stimulation or inhibition depends on peculiar properties of the muscles or glands which they affect. All cells may be stimulated by low concentrations of ACh. Slightly elevated concentrations become inhibitory to some, while for others the level of ACh must be much higher before reversal of effect occurs. Assuming that a neuron releases a given amount of transmitting agent, the effect on the cell will depend on whether the critical level for reversal is low or high. It has been shown that isolated heart muscle which has been washed completely free of ACh is actually stimulated by addition of very minute amounts, and only very slight increases are required for inhibition. In the body, vagal stimulation normally results in ACh production to surpass the stimulating level. On the other hand, cholinergic nerves are incapable of producing enough ACh to reach inhibitory levels for those muscle cells of the intestine. Inhibition may only be observed by the experimental addition of quantities above those found under normal conditions.

In expansion on this theory, it is noted that cholinesterase is present in fluids surrounding the cells within the body. In order to be effective, ACh would have to be produced in sufficient quantities so that not all is destroyed before reaching the structure on which it is to act. If extracellular cholinesterase is at a high concentration, most ACh is destroyed and only a small (stimulatory) amount reaches the cell in transmission. Lower levels of extracellular cholinesterase would result in less ACh destruction, so that a greater amount (inhibitory) reaches the final target cell. It must be realized that these and many other points of question regarding neural and synaptic transmission must await further investigative evidence before widely acceptable theories will be available.

ADDITIONAL READING

ECCLES, SIR JOHN, "The Synapse," *Scientific American* 212:56-66, 1965.
McLENNAN, HUGH, *Synaptic Transmission,* Philadelphia: W. B. Saunders Co., 1963.

CHAPTER 5

General action of receptors

While all protoplasm may be stimulated by a variety of conditions, cells becoming specialized for particular functions display increasing sensitivity to certain changes in their environment. Cells that become especially sensitive to a particular type of stimulation are called receptors. The type of stimulus to which the receptor normally responds, for instance, heat, cold, light, is referred to as the *adequate stimulus*. It is possible that the receptor may respond to another type of changing condition, but the strength of the stimulus in that instance must be much greater. That type of stimulus is the *inadequate stimulus*. Thus, a piece of dry ice placed against the skin may cause the sensation of heat because the extreme rate at which heat is lost may be sufficient to act as an inadequate stimulus to receptors for warmth. It should be emphasized here that the receptor is merely the structure which responds to the stimulus and initiates impulses which may proceed along a nerve. The manner in which those impulses are interpreted when they reach a particular region of the brain will determine the actual sensation of which we are conscious.

CLASSIFICATION OF RECEPTORS

The most obvious means of classifying receptors is based *on the nature of the stimulating agent or condition* (page 21). According to this classification one would recognize four types of receptors:

1. *Mechanoreceptors*—those stimulated by mechanical force, either pressure or stretch

2. *Thermoreceptors*—those stimulated by a gain or loss of heat energy, generally imparting the sensation of warmth or cold
3. *Chemoreceptors*—receptors stimulated by the presence of chemical substances in solution, most frequently thought of in relation to sensations of taste and smell
4. *Photoreceptors*—cells specialized for stimulation by light; generally related to vision in humans, but in other forms of life sensitivity exists to light wave lengths invisible to the human eye

Although certain animals possess electric organs by means of which considerable electric current may be generated, it is not probable that specific electroreceptors exist; nevertheless, electrical stimulation may be employed as the inadequate stimulus to a wide variety of receptors.

Receptors may also be classified *according to the source of the stimulation.* In this manner three types are recognized:

1. *Exteroceptors*—receptors that receive their stimulus directly from the external environment, such as those for vision and temperature sense
2. *Enteroceptors*—receptors stimulated indirectly from the external environment but located within the body, such as mechanoreceptors of the lung and digestive system
3. *Proprioceptors*—receptors receiving their stimulus from some condition truly within the body, such as receptors of muscles and joints concerned with coordinated movement and equilibrium

From the classification above it should be apparent that conscious sensations will not always result from the stimulation of receptors. Those receptors related to sensations function in close conjunction with our so-called senses and sense organs such as the eye, ear or skin. Some receptors when stimulated initiate impulses which are eventually important for actions of internal organs but do not result in sensation. These receptors are also referred to as *activators.* Activators responding to mechanical and chemical stimuli within the body are concerned with proper breathing, digestive action and circulation of the blood.

THE NATURE OF THE RECEPTOR RESPONSE

Most of the earlier information on receptor function was gained through studies on the impulses being conducted by neurons leading from the receptors. As will be indicated later, that information is useful for certain interpretations but would be quite misleading in reference to the true nature of the receptor response. It will be recalled that the impulse, as it is conducted over the neuron, is of an all-or-none character; that is, once initiated the spike intensity and rate of conduction are of a nature peculiar to the particular neuron. The response of the receptor on stimulation is quite different.

The nature of the receptor function on stimulation may be illustrated in the type of response recorded from stretch receptors of crustaceans. These receptors are associated with muscle cells in the claws and are adequately stimulated by stretching in opposite directions the attached ends of muscle fibers. If the stimulus is applied while electrodes are in contact with the receptor it is seen that repeated-spike potentials result from a stimulus of constant intensity, and it should be recognized that these spikes are characteristic of the conducting neuron (Figure 13). In order to examine the true receptor activity the structure is

Fig. 13. A. Stretch receptor of crustacean claw; receptor (r), muscle fiber (m); arrows indicate direction of stretch stimulus. B. Record of generator potential with novocaine present to prevent spike potential. Stimulus applied and discontinued at (a) and (b) respectively. C. Normal response to stretch with repeated spike potentials arising from generator potentials.

treated with novocaine, which prevents the appearance of the spike but allows the normal receptor function. Following such treatment the stimulation has resulted in a slight depolarization which remains steady during the brief period of stretch; this is the *generator response*. The generator response is a graded response rather than all-or-none as is the spike in the conducting neuron. The strength of the generator response varies directly with the strength of the stimulus.

Another example of receptor activity may help clarify certain points regarding the relation of the receptor to the neuron response. The Pacinian corpuscle serves as a receptor for pressure. Because of its large size—as much as a millimeter in diameter—this receptor with its associated nerve is exposed and removed from the body for study with relative ease. The receptor consists of a laminated-cellular enclosure of the neuron ending. As the nerve fiber leaves the Pacinian corpuscle it becomes myelinated and displays regularly constricted nodes of Ranvier. By careful micromanipulation it is possible to strip the Pacinian corpuscle partially away to expose the neuron so electrodes may be placed on it and at the positions of each of several nodes. As the intensity of the stimulus (pressure) is increased, the intensity of the generator potential is increased (Figure 14), but the impulse in the neuron is an all-or-none spike. Apparently, similar types of depolarization characteristics are seen in other kinds of receptors and their associated neurons.

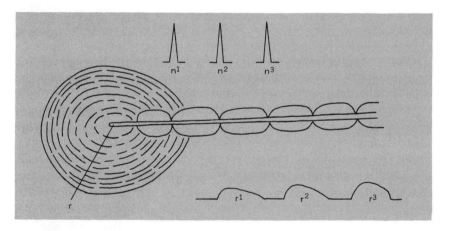

Fig. 14. The Pacinian corpuscle with its associated neuron and receptor's region (r). Graded generator potentials with increasing stimulus intensity (r_1, r_2, r_3), spike potentials at nodes (n_1, n_2, n_3).

Less information is available regarding the factors involved in the development of generator potentials. Ionic involvement may be different than in neurons, at least the graded potential may occur even with considerable reduction of extracellular sodium. Although there is evidence for the presence of cholinesterase in the laminated structure of the Pacinian corpuscle, proof for the involvement of ACh is required.

IMPULSE CONDUCTION AND RECEPTOR FUNCTION

While the generator potential represents the actual function of the receptor, the relation of the receptor to the body's coordination will eventually depend on impulses which are carried from the region of the stimulus to other portions of the body. Recording of neuron action potentials indicates how the receptor's action eventually relates to the rest of the organism.

Within limitations, the number of impulses conducted over the neuron per unit time relates directly to the strength of the stimulus acting on the receptor (Figure 15A). As more impulses are carried to the brain, in the instance of stimulating a receptor related to a conscious sensation, that area of the brain interprets them as a stronger stimulus. In many instances, impulses are carried through a series of several neurons and eventually to muscle tissue where the impulses result in contraction and movement. As the stimulus to the receptor is stronger, more impulses eventually reach the muscle to cause a stronger reaction. The number of impulses will, of course, relate to the intensity of the graded generator potential.

The number of impulses which progress from a receptor by way of its neuron will not remain constant for an indefinite period of time, even though the intensity of the stimulus remains unchanged. As illustrated in Figure 15B, the number of impulses will diminish with the passage of time, and this is indicative of changes relating to *adaptation.* This is easily recognized in the instance of conscious sensation, for as the stimulus continues we become less aware of its presence. Light pressure on the skin is less apparent in passing time, and taste sensation diminishes when a flavored solution is held in the mouth. The nature of the neural conduction furnishes an explanation for the adaptation phenomenon, for as fewer impulses travel over the nerve per unit time, this will approximate the condition of weaker and weaker stimulation. Adaptation apparently is not synonymous with fatigue, for as a structure becomes fatigued the application of a stronger stimulus will not restore activity to the original level as it will in the instance of an adapting receptor.

Receptors vary considerably in the rate at which they adapt. Photoreceptors will adapt in a fraction of a second. In order to offset this

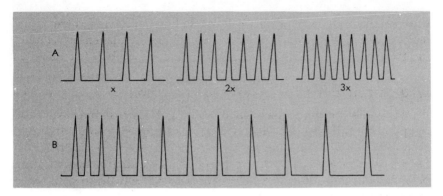

Fig. 15. Receptor function indicated by impulses over its neuron. A. Increasing impulses per unit time as the stimulus is increased from X to 2X to 3X intensity. B. Impulses indicating adaptation.

rapid adaptation the receptor must be moved constantly so a different stimulus is presented. In the human eye this is normally accomplished by movements which are neither detectable nor disturbing to vision. Touch receptors in the skin also adapt quite rapidly. Conversely, receptors for pain adapt very slowly, requiring many minutes of constant stimulation before the frequency of impulse conduction decreases appreciably. It is fortunate that adaptation is slow in that instance, for more rapid adaptation would result in less awareness of a damaging condition within a brief period of time. If one were to withstand the initial discomfort until adaptation had occurred, one would then be able to ignore the painful stimulus and considerable damage of the tissues might result.

ADDITIONAL READING

ALTMAN, JOSEPH, *Organic Foundations of Animal Behavior*, New York: Holt, Rinehart & Winston, Inc., 1966, pp. 111-167.
KENNEDY, DONALD, "The Initiation of Impulses in Receptors," *American Zoologist* 2:27-43, 1962.

CHAPTER 6

Mechanoreceptors and thermoreceptors

THE NATURE OF MECHANORECEPTORS

The response of an amoeba to gentle touch indicates that undifferentiated protoplasm is sensitive to mechanical stimulation. Streaming movement will come to a temporary halt, there being a latent period between the time the stimulus is applied and the response is noted. This latent period becomes shorter as the strength of the stimulus is increased. Mechanoreception in Paramecium is indicated by its backing away after striking an object in swimming. Other interesting responses in this ciliate are its negative geotropism, that is, its oriented swimming in a direction opposite to that of gravitational force and its tendency to swim into gentle fluid currents. It may be that the cell's cilia are in some way related to these reactions; however, this is more probably true for cirri of hypotrichs such as Euplotes. While locomotor organella of the protozoa may help somewhat in mechanoreception, that specific function is more easily recognized in the role of specialized structures in higher forms of life.

The simplest type of mechanoreceptor is the *bare nerve ending*. Structures of this type are found among the epithelial cells in the earthworm. They are also seen lying beneath the epidermis in the vertebrates, but in all instances, they are considered as primitive types of receptors. In man these bare nerve endings are associated with sensation of pain. While they may be stimulated by mechanical means, other types of stimuli may also be effective, indicating their lesser specialization in the requirement of a particularly adequate stimulus.

Bare nerve endings may also serve as receptors without the necessity of the stimulus being directly applied. Sensory hairs, actually cuticular extensions, in the joint regions of the arthropods have closely associated nerve endings which are stimulated when the hairs are displaced. Insect spines also have nerve endings at their base. In mammals there are nerve endings about the hair root which may be stimulated as the hair is touched and bent. In these instances, the structure with which the nerve ending is associated acts as a lever to increase the pressure brought on the receptor cell.

Muscle spindles of the type shown in Figure 16D are seen in mammalian tissue, but essentially the same types of structures may be found in lower forms. The receptor is a modified muscle cell with many bare neuron endings on its surface. The adequate stimulus is supplied by stretching the spindle at its opposite ends. This results in generator potentials and the transmission of spike potentials along the neuron. Muscle spindles have been mentioned previously in relation to reactions

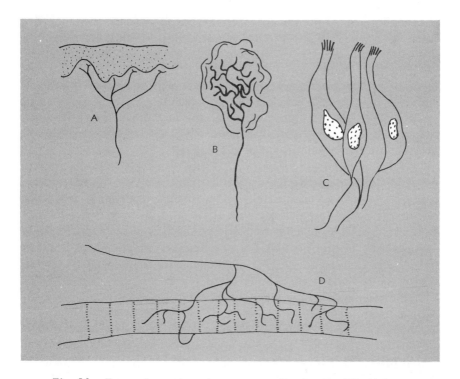

Fig. 16. Types of receptors: bare nerve ending in skin (A), Meissner corpuscle (B), ciliated receptors from the earthworm (C), muscle spindle (D).

in which the tension of surrounding muscle fibers is increased with resulting adjustment of body position.

Some receptors exist as *capsule-like enclosures* about the neuron ending. The Pacinian corpuscle, which was discussed in relation to the general function of receptors (Figure 14, page 41), is an example of such a structure. Pressure on the connective tissue about the neuron results in stimulation. These types of receptors are associated with pressure sensation in vertebrates.

Receptors of the *ciliated* type display a wide distribution and specialization for a great variety of functions. In the simplest form these receptors, seen in the epithelial region of the earthworm, consist of bipolar neurons with short cilia extending at the surface for stimulation from the environment. It is interesting to note that very similar types of cells may also function as chemoreceptors. Ciliated receptor cells show their greatest degree of development in relation to sense organs serving hearing and equilibrium. In these instances, the mechanical stimulus is generally furnished through fluid displacement about the cilia or as a result of adjacent particulate matter which bears on the cilia as a result of gravitational force.

FUNCTIONS SERVED BY MECHANORECEPTORS

The basic types of mechanoreceptors which have been described will show considerable variation, and a specific type of response may not be assigned to a receptor merely on the basis of its structure; however, regardless of the particular sense which the receptor may serve, the stimulus is mechanical in all instances.

General sensations of *touch* and *pressure* are for the most part due to the stimulation of receptors in the skin and therefore relatively close to the body surface. Of course, it is impossible to assign a particular sensation in lower forms of life, but stimulation of bare nerve endings and ciliated cells in annelids or hairlike receptors in arthropods results in movements of an orientative or avoidance type. In mammals receptors of a type similar to those found in man probably are related to the same sensations which we identify through our conscious interpretation.

Bare nerve endings serving the sensation of *pain* are found in high numbers and uniform distribution over the body surface. *Meisner's corpuscles* are stimulated by very light pressure and are associated with our sense of touch. These receptors are more numerous at the fingertips, around the lips and on the side of the nose; they are more numerous at the extremities, decreasing in number in progression toward the body. Acuity of tactile sense varies directly with the number of receptors per unit of skin area. Pacinian corpuscles are located deeper within the skin, and therefore a greater force is required for their stimulation. They are associated with the sensation of deep pressure. Pacinian corpuscles and bare nerve endings are also found within the digestive system where their mechanical stimulation due to the presence of food and digestion mixtures will lead to essential changes in function of digestive organs without conscious awareness.

Proprioceptive function, related to the adjustment of body position and coordinated movement, is highly dependent on receptors found in the muscles, tendons and joints. Muscle spindles serve the so-called muscle sense, not a conscious sensation at all but rather a means by which the muscles are adjusted in their degree of contraction in maintenance of posture. Tendon reflexes are initiated by the stimulation of very similar structures in the tendons, joining muscles to bone. The knee-jerk reflex follows the striking of the patellar tendon below the knee cap. This results in a stretching of the tendon and its associated receptors. Impulses resulting from that stimulus proceed through a series of many neurons until they are finally carried to muscles in the leg, causing the kick response. Pacinian corpuscles and bare nerve endings in the tendons and joints serve similar functions. In all of these instances, the displacement of a portion of the body results in stimulation of receptors and impulses which are eventually carried to muscles whose contractions cause the necessary compensating adjustments without conscious effort.

Many types of orientation reactions are seen in animals, and some of these relate to mechanical stimulation. *Stereotaxic* responses are those resulting from contact with a substrate or adjacent object. Insect larvae show this response, crawling in a straight line in a space between two objects but seeking that contact again in swaying motions on reaching the end of a restricting maze. This type of behavior may well be protective to these forms since they tend to remain in crevices and in close contact with objects furnishing some cover. Stimulation of mechanoreceptors is important in orientation of snails and starfish, and a righting reaction is initiated if they are deprived of substrate contact.

Rheotactic responses are those to a stream of water. Planaria respond in a positive manner to a gentle current, moving toward its source as a result of stimulation of epithelial mechanoreceptors. Possible evidence for the sensory function of cilia in Paramecium is seen in the fact that the organism will usually move into a very gentle fluid current. Rheotaxis is clearly illustrated in the response of a fish which in the resting condition will always face upstream. Its orientation is due in part to skin receptors, especially those of the lateral line, although visual stimuli are also important. Blind fish do not respond in this manner unless in contact with a substrate; therefore, the stimulation is furnished as the current carries them along, resulting in friction.

Anemotaxis is the orientation to air currents. In flying insects adjustments in posture and direction are closely related to the function of mechanoreceptors in the antennae.

Geotaxis is the response to gravitational force. Animals which move with the force of gravity are positively geotropic. Burrowing marine worms serve as an example. Those animals which move opposite to the force of gravity display negative geotropism. Many ciliated protozoa behave in this manner, although lacking the type of receptor which accounts for the response in metazoa. The fundamental structure for geotropic responses depends on the presence of a particulate body which through the force of gravity is brought to bear on hair cells. The *statocyst* in the marginal region of the medusoid coelenterates represents the simplest form of these sensory organs (Figure 17). As the animal

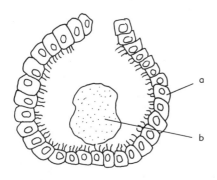

Fig. 17. Diagrammatic statocyst: Ciliated receptor cell (a), statolith (b).

is tilted to one side or the other, different receptor cells are stimulated and this relates to its ability to maintain an upright position. Removal of the marginal statocysts results in a loss of coordinated swimming and geotactic responses.

A similar type of receptor is seen in the base of antennules of crustaceans. Since these structures are a portion of the exoskeleton they are lost during molting. Their reestablishment with the formation of a new exoskeleton requires the introduction of a new *statolith,* normally a grain of sand. If the animals are maintained in a clean aquarium and iron filings furnished rather than sand, those structures become functional statoliths following a molt. By holding a magnet above the animal it may actually be caused to turn upside down as a result of the unusual stimulation to the statocyst.

Statocysts of similar types are found in almost all invertebrates and vertebrates. In the vertebrate ear the structures are located within the fluid which fills the membranous labyrinth. The sense organ is the *macula,* which consists of a cluster of hair cells on which rest a number of calcium carbonate granules or *otoliths.* Within each ear are two such maculae, one of which is on a horizontal plane, the other vertically oriented. These structures are in mirror arrangement in the opposite ears, so tilting the head in any direction will result in changes in the nature of the stimulus furnished by the otoliths of each macula.

The sense organs so far described are especially suited to serve the sense of *static equilibrium,* that is, the sense of position in space. They are not, however, as efficient in serving the sense of *dynamic equilibrium* which relates to movement in space. Structures serving dynamic equilibrium are seen in the inner ear of vertebrates. Within the *ampullae* of the *semicircular canals* (Figure 19) are the *cupolae* which contain hair cells whose projections extend into a gelatinous covering, the *crista.* The entire structure is surrounded by fluid which is set into motion by angular rotation of the head. Sudden movement results in a flow of fluid in the opposite direction, due to its inertia, with the result that the crista is bent and the hair cells stimulated. If the movement is slowly accelerated the fluid tends to move with the semicircular canals and no stimulus results. With that condition existing, a sudden change in direction or cessation of the angular movement results in continued flow of fluid through the semicircular canals, and a stimulation is effected. In the higher vertebrates the three semicircular canals in each ear are arranged at right angles to each other in the three possible planes of movement. Through this arrangement angular movement forward, backward or tilting or rotating to the left or right will result in the stimulation of receptor cells in one of the semicircular canals.

Phonoreception, while generally related to the sense of hearing, may also be discussed at this time since the stimulus involved is a mechanical one. In this instance, the stimulus is transmitted in waves through an air or liquid medium. These waves originate from sound and progress from that point as alternating condensations and rarifications of the transmitting medium. The number of these waves passing a point in a given time is referred to as the *frequency* and is expressed in cycles per second (cps). In the instance of human sensations we interpret these frequencies as they relate to pitch. The human ear contains receptors which are stimulated by frequencies from about 40 cps, a low pitch, to approximately 20,000 cps, a high pitch. Other vertebrates are sensitive to quite different ranges. The dog may respond to sounds at 35,000 cps, and bats may detect frequencies as high as 70,000 to 100,000 cps with great accuracy. Although interpretation of sound in the invertebrates may be open to question, they do respond to vibratory stimuli although generally of lower frequency. Insect responses are seen in ranges from about 30 up to 30,000 cps. Some caterpillars appear sensitive to vibrations of 30 to 1000 cps. The organs, the portions of which may be set into motion by these vibrations, are quite varied, but the receptor in all instances is a type of hair cell.

Hairy caterpillars respond to appropriate frequencies at much lower intensity than do relatively hairless ones. Mosquitoes react to vibrations which affect fine hairs of the antennae. The stimulus in either instance is applied to receptor cells not unlike those which have been considered earlier in this section. Most notable of the insect auditory structures are the *tympanic organs* which may be found in the thoracic or abdominal regions or in the tibia of the appendages. In all instances, the organ consists of a thin cuticular membrane covering an underlying air sac. Air vibrations set the tympanic membrane into motion and this in turn furnishes a mechanical stimulation to the receptor cells. The receptor cells are actually bipolar neurons with terminal filaments which transmit the mechanical force. These and other cellular elements make up the *scolopidia* which generally serve in phonoreception of the insects.

Aquatic animals enjoy a particular advantage over terrestrial insects in phonoreception because vibrations in a fluid medium are much

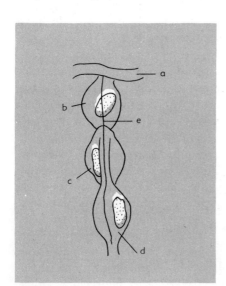

Fig. 18. The scolopidium of an insect: tympanum (a), cap cell (b), sheath cell (c), receptor cell (d), filament (e).

more easily transmitted into tissues to affect the mechanoreceptor. Fish possess ear structures not unlike those of higher vertebrates, and vibratory stimuli are effective to their receptors much in the same manner. It is also apparent that other receptors in the skin are stimulated by vibrations. These structures, of general distribution and also concentrated in the lateral line, are stimulated by frequencies of less than 100 cps. As a result of their stimulation a fish may strike at a food organism several inches away or maintain its proper spatial position in relation to others swimming in schools.

Land-dwelling vertebrates indirectly enjoy the advantage of aquatic forms in phonoreception by the location of their receptors within the fluids of the inner ear. Air vibrations reaching the ear strike the *tympanic membrane* which in turn activates the middle ear bones, or *ossicles.* These function as a lever system to increase the force of the vibrations so they are transmitted into the fluids of the inner ear. The vibrations indirectly affect hair cells in the *organ of Corti.* The organ of Corti lies on the *basilar membrane,* both of which extend the length of the *cochlea.* Fine fibers run across the basilar membrane, and these are set into motion by the vibrations within the fluid. This results in a movement of the hair cells of the organ of Corti, and they are stimulated by the resistance of the surrounding fluid. Mammals are capable of appreciation of differences in a wide range of pitch since the fibers of the basilar membrane vary in length, being short at the base of the cochlea and of progressively greater length toward its apex. Vibrations of higher frequency set the shorter fibers into motion, and this accounts for the stimulation of receptor cells in a particular region of the organ of Corti. The impulses, as they reach a specific portion of the brain over a given neuron, will be interpreted as a sound of particular pitch. From this it should be apparent that the greater cochlear length in the higher vertebrates furnishes a better opportunity for graded variation in basilar fiber length and eventually in greater phonoreceptor discrimination.

THERMORECEPTORS

Receptors serving the temperature sense are not recognized in as great a variety of form as are those for mechanoreception. In mammals the receptors are encapsulated structures identified as *Ruffini endings* and *Krause end bulbs* for sensations of warmth and cold, respectively. In the sharks and their relatives sensory bulbs in the head region respond by increasing the frequency of impulse discharge on cooling; decreased activity occurs with warming. Structures in the lateral line

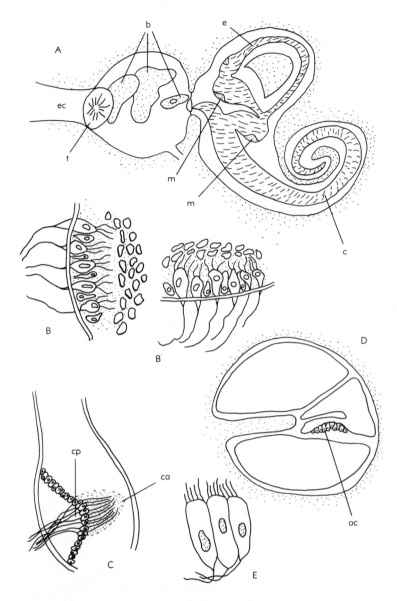

Fig. 19. Diagrammatic representation of the vertebrate ear:
A. Entire view showing external canal (ec), tympanic membrane (t), middle ear bones (b), semicircular canal (e) of membranous labyrinth, location of maculae (m, m') cochlea (c). B, B'. Details of maculae at m. m'. C. Detail of cupola (cp) and crista (ca) in ampulla of semicircular canal. D. Cross section of cochlea, enlarged, to show position of organ of Corti (oc). E. Detail of hair cells of organ of Corti.

of some of the bony fishes respond to temperature changes, but in this instance, the impulse discharge rate varies directly with the temperature of the water. Amphibia probably possess skin receptors for the temperature sense which are distinct from the mechanoreceptors, but their exact nature has not been established.

The stimulation of a thermoreceptor depends on the loss or gain of heat energy, and that change is due to the existing *temperature gradient*. A temperature gradient exists when there is a difference in heat energy content of adjacent bodies or areas, and the heat energy will be dissipated from the region of its greater level into that of its lesser level. The greater the gradient or difference in temperature, the greater will be the rate at which heat energy will be transmitted. It follows that with the passage of time the gradient would diminish, and therefore the rate at which further temperature changes occur would diminish proportionally.

The effective stimulation of a thermoreceptor depends not on the temperature of the environmental air or water or of some object touched but rather on the specific temperature gradient furnished. If the skin, which is normally at a temperature of about 28°C., is cooled to 20°C. by previous exposure to cold and then touched by an object at 24°C., that object will feel warm as a result of the inward temperature gradient or heat energy transfer. If the skin had been at normal temperature the object at 24°C. would have felt cool due to the outward temperature gradient. The adequate stimulus for Ruffini endings has been determined as a rise in temperature of 0.001°C. per second for at least 3 seconds; for Krause end bulbs the adequate stimulus is a fall in temperature of 0.004°C. per second for the same period of time. It will be noticed that if the skin is exposed to a change in temperature the original sensation of warmth or cold diminishes with time. This may be attributed to the receptor's adaptation and also to the lessening stimulation as the skin temperature approaches that of the environment, causing the temperature gradient to be less. Of course, an extreme temperature gradient might be sufficient to act as an inadequate stimulus to a thermoreceptor and result in false sensations of heat or cold.

Protozoa are sensitive to temperature changes of a few degrees; they will seek a more desirable environment if regions of the culture are warmed or cooled. The development of thermoreceptors leads to greater sensitivity. Leeches approach warmer areas with a 3°C. gradient; insects may respond to changes of 1°C. or less, and there is evidence for difference in receptor discharge in fishes with temperature changes of 0.5°C. Thermoreceptors in the head region of some snakes are so sensitive that they are stimulated by body heat of warm-blooded animals and aid in accurate direction of striking at prey even in the dark.

ADDITIONAL READING

HOAR, WILLIAM S., *General and Comparative Physiology*, Englewood Cliffs, N. J.: Prentice-Hall, Inc., 1966, pp. 503-523.

CHAPTER 7

Chemoreceptors and photoreceptors

Chemoreceptors and photoreceptors share a common property in that the stimulating agent or the action of the stimulus is related to a specific chemical or group of chemical substances. The presence of that substance, or a change in its structure, is in some way responsible for the development of the generator potential. It must be remembered, however, that the mere origin of impulses along a nerve is not sufficient for the final response. The conscious interpretation depends finally on the function of nerve cells in a particular region of the brain or a similar organ. For that reason, it should not always be assumed that chemical stimulation will result in taste or smell sensations as we are aware of them.

CHEMORECEPTORS

It is essential that chemical substances be in solution if they are to stimulate a receptor. This is easily visualized in the aquatic forms but even for those not living in water the stimulating agent is dissolved in fluids which bathe or surround the receptor cells. The molecular character of the stimulating agent is important. Acetic acid, which ionizes to only a slight degree and therefore exists to a large extent in the molecular form, tastes much more sour at similar molarity than does hydrochloric acid, which exists mainly in the ionized condition. Older theories held that the presence of certain groups within a molecule were essential in imparting a sweet taste. More recently, molecular configuration, sizes and shapes have been indicated as important in the stimulation of certain types of chemoreceptors. These ideas may relate to specificity of the chemical stimulant to some agent in the membrane much in the same manner that ACh bears a "fit" relation to cholinesterase for stimulation effects. Confirmation of this through the identity of specific cellular components is presently lacking, however, and the apparent existence of water receptors in some mammals would be difficult to relate to high specificity which would be expected in an enzymatic theory.

All cells display sensitivity to their chemical environment. The solution which bathes cells, either within the body or isolated *in vitro*, must be of particular composition not only for osmotic balance but also in regard to particular ions. If the ionic balance is altered the cells may change significantly in their appearance and action. Within vertebrates *common chemical sense* is important in that protein in the stomach may bring about functional changes relating to digestion, and alteration in the concentration of hydrogen ion, carbon dioxide or oxygen in the blood stream will stimulate particular cells and result in changes in breathing or circulatory action. Although we are not aware of these stimuli and the responses which follow, they are of extreme importance in coordination of functions essential for the maintenance of normal body conditions.

Protozoa show a variety of responses which indicate their sensitivity to chemical stimulation. In the presence of monovalent cations such as Na and K, ciliary movement is reversed, and swimming becomes erratic. Paramecium reacts in a positive manner to carbon dioxide, the cells accumulating in large numbers about a bubble of gas under a cover slip. It would appear that amoeboid species are especially sensitive to chemical characteristics of food organisms, for a high degree of selectivity is displayed in food intake. Ciliates and flagellates are selected or bypassed with remarkable species differentiation.

Coelenterates are sensitive to chemical stimulation as is seen in the strong feeding reactions when meat juices are placed in their environment. Of a large number of specific chemical compounds which have been tried, sulfur-containing cysteine and glutathione are especially effective in causing this response. Even isolated tentacles of Hydra will show these reactions when so exposed, indicating the general distribution of the receptors. Echinoderms show similar chemical sensitivity, and there is a tendency in these forms and the higher coelenterates for chemoreceptors to become localized about the mouth region.

While chemoreceptors are generally distributed over the surface of flatworms and annelids, there is some indication of their concentration in particular areas. Planaria will seek out food in their environment through the use of the chemoreceptors located in the anterior region of the body. Such reception also plays a role in food selection by the annelids. Although sensitivity exists over the body, the receptors are concentrated in the buccal and pharyngeal areas. In these forms the receptor cells bear a similarity to those of higher forms, generally consisting of *hair cells* directly exposed to the environment.

Fishes and amphibia are generally sensitive to chemical stimulation over the entire body surface, but in these forms specific regions of chemoreceptor concentration are easily recognized. Structures similar to those serving taste and smell in mammals are recognized in the mouth and nasal pits of the fish, and taste buds and olfactory receptors are present in the mouth and nasal regions of the frog.

Crustaceans have hairlike chemoreceptors located on the antennules and mouth parts. It is by means of these that particles of food placed in the water at some distance may be detected, although their products are in extreme dilution. The chemoreceptors of the limbs, proboscis and antennae of insects account for much of their behavior. The seeking of food, identification of normal inhabitants of a colony and localization for mating purposes all depend on chemical sense. In some moths the male may be attracted to the female from distances of more than a mile as a result of chemical substances released from the female scent gland.

While chemical sense exists in birds, it is poorly developed as compared to other forms of life. They depend mainly on their acute sense of vision for the localization of food and general orientation.

The *olfactory sense* (smell) in man and other mammals is served by ciliated cells in the uppermost region of the nasal cavity. This location is important in that the receptors are protected from overexposure to stimulants which might be injurious at high concentration. Since in normal breathing less air comes into that area, sniffing, a rapid air intake, may be necessary to bring gaseous material to the area in sufficient concentration for detection. Solubility of the chemical stimulant is effected in the mucus layer of the tissues. The olfactory receptors are peculiar in consisting of *bipolar neurons* which come into direct contact with the external environment. For this reason, it is proposed that they not only are affected by stimulants but may also be a means for the entrance of infective agents directly into the nervous system. Impulses from these receptors need be carried only a short distance to the brain, and the same proximity, it has been held, may be of significance for brain invasion.

While olfactory receptors display a certain specificity for particular molecular stimulation, the nature of the conscious interpretation is probably less exact as a result of a blending interpretation by the brain. Many classifications for basic odors have been presented, recognizing such interpretations as floral, ethereal, mint, spicy, camphoric, musky, pungent and putrid. Since interpretation is largely a matter of individual variation, a classification based on the specificity of molecular structure in its relation to certain receptors seems the most promising method of grouping, rather than depending on the interpretive function of the brain for conscious sensation.

The *gustatory sense* (taste) is more easily defined. In the instance of humans, it has long been recognized that chemical substances may

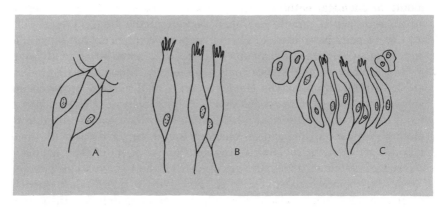

Fig. 20. Chemoreceptors: A. Rodlike receptor cells from insect olfactory pit. B. Mammalian olfactory receptors. C. Taste bud of the tongue showing ciliated receptors and supporting cells.

be distinguished as imparting one of four basic tastes: sweet, salt, sour or bitter. The receptors are ciliated cells of *taste buds* which are located mainly on the upper surface of the tongue, although receptors are also found in certain regions of the throat. Within the taste bud the receptor cell is recognized as a distinct structure whose stimulation gives rise to generator potentials and these in turn cause the development of impulses in separate but closely associated neurons. Supporting cells in the taste bud are continuously in division and with maturation become receptor cells; thus, although the life of a receptor cell proper may be only a few days at most, this is offset by their constant replacement.

Specificity of receptor function is more easily demonstrated for the gustatory than the olfactory sense. The basic tastes are imparted by particular types of materials. Sugars cause a sweet sensation, and this has been related to the presence of particular configurations in their molecules; on the other hand, it is difficult to reconcile the sweet taste which chloroform imparts with structural similarity to a carbohydrate.

Salty taste results from inorganic chlorides, bromides and other similar materials in solution. Sour is generally related to acid materials, although hydrogen ion and pH are not necessarily of greatest importance. It will be recalled that acetic acid tastes more sour, although hydrochloric acid is stronger in terms of its ionization. Bitter tastes are caused by alkaloids such as quinine; however, that sensation is not restricted to the presence of such plant products, for ether has a bitter taste as well.

While exceptions exist in the attempted classification of taste according to chemical nature, there is additional evidence to indicate that receptors are specifically related to their stimulants and resulting sensation. Substances in solution must be placed on a particular region of the tongue in order to be tasted. Sweet taste is detected on the tip of the tongue, salt on the tip and sides, sour on the sides and bitter at the back of the tongue. If the mouth is rinsed with a solution containing two types of chemical substances, both tastes are distinguished rather than a blending as occurs in the olfactory sense. Furthermore, electrodes placed in contact with neurons leading from receptors in a particular portion of the tongue indicate the passage of impulses mainly following the application of a particular type of material on the tongue's surface. Through such studies, evidence has been presented for the existence of receptors that are stimulated by the presence of water. Water sensitivity has also been attributed to some of the insects, but such direct evidence for the existence of specific receptors has not been as clearly furnished.

PHOTORECEPTORS

Photoreception in any form of life depends on properties of light and its relation to matter. Sense organs for vision merely become more complex as they differentiate to serve organisms in a better manner. The basic principles remain the same from the simplest form to the highest vertebrates. It is essential that one understand the basic properties of light in order to appreciate the various structures developed.

Light energy moves through a given medium in a straight line but in a vibratory manner. The regular frequency of the vibrations enables one to characterize light by its *wave length,* most frequently expressed in millimicron units (mu). The human eye can detect light in the visible spectrum ranging from about 400 to 700 mu. Longer (infrared) and shorter (ultraviolet) wave lengths are not seen but may have an effect on the eye, causing general damage to the tissues if exposure is prolonged. Except for birds and some fishes and primates, it is questionable whether other animals perceive colors as does man. Our ability to distinguish color leads to the description of the sensations imparted by the various wave lengths: 400 mu as violet, 450 mu as blue, 510 mu as green, 550 mu as yellow, 650 mu as orange and 685 mu as red. Animals which do not perceive colors in the same manner may, nevertheless, receive stimulation at particular wave lengths. Insects are sensitive to the shorter wave lengths and are strongly attracted by ultraviolet light at about 385 mu. Lacking evidence for color vision in other forms does not exclude the possibility that a range of wave lengths may be stimulatory, but the effect is probably one of variation in stimulation intensity with different wave lengths rather than color.

In order to be effective as a stimulating force light must be *absorbed* in some manner. Matter varies in its capacity to absorb light of different wave lengths. If white light, which is actually a mixture

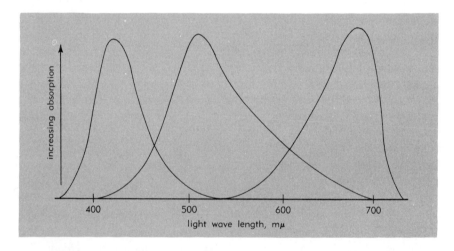

Fig. 21. Light absorption in the visible spectrum by three hypothetical materials. If photoreceptors are present which absorb maximally at 510μ, different intensities of green are perceived. With receptors present which contain materials absorbing maximally at 410, 510 or 685μ, specifically to each then appreciation of different colors might be possible.

of light of all wave lengths, is allowed to shine through a colored solution, the color which we detect depends on the light of a particular wave length which was *transmitted* or passed through the solution The other wave lengths were absorbed by the chemical substance in solution.

As light is absorbed by a molecule its energy is imparted to that molecule with the result that chemical changes are effected. This ability to *evoke chemical change* upon absorption is the underlying principle of photoreception. Photoreceptive cells would, therefore, be expected to contain chemical substances absorbing light, and the resulting chemical change in some manner related to the stimulation. For color vision it would be necessary that several distinct types of photoreceptors, each with its peculiar chemical substance for light absorption at a particular wave length, would have to be present. On the other hand, a single type of receptor and chemical for light absorption would lead only to sensations of varying degrees of light intensity when stimulated by wave lengths shorter or longer than those of maximum absorption.

Light also may be *reflected* from a surface. This is the opposite of its absorption. Since white light strikes matter only, that which is reflected reaches photoreceptors for stimulation. The color which we appreciate in our surroundings is due to absorbing and reflecting light of different wave lengths. A perfect mirror reflects all the light, thus giving a true picture of the object before it.

The amount of light coming from a source may be very slight and must be concentrated into a smaller area in order to furnish sufficient energy for excitation. This concentration is effected by *lenses* of different types of transmitting material. Lenses owe their result to the fact that light, on passing from one medium into another, is bent or *refracted* at the media surfaces to continue through the second medium in a straight line but a slightly different direction. The curvature of lenses, either of living or nonliving material, acts on the incoming light so that under perfect conditions it is concentrated in a conelike manner from a circular field of origin, thus effecting the required concentration on a smaller area with greater intensity and stimulating force. It is for this purpose that the eyes of higher forms of life become more complex in their structure and therefore more efficient in function. The basic principle of photoreceptor cell function remains the same in all forms of life.

There is a great variation in the specific chemical substances which act to absorb light in photoreceptors of different animals. Most of those which have been investigated belong to a group of substances referred to as *carotenoids*. Some of these, such as xanthophyll and astaxanthin are responsible for the yellow color of vegetation in the fall or red color of tomatoes, respectively. A well-known carotenoid is *beta-carotene* which may be split on hydrolysis into two molecules of vitamin A_1. Vitamin A_2 is of similar structure but has another double bond in the ring.

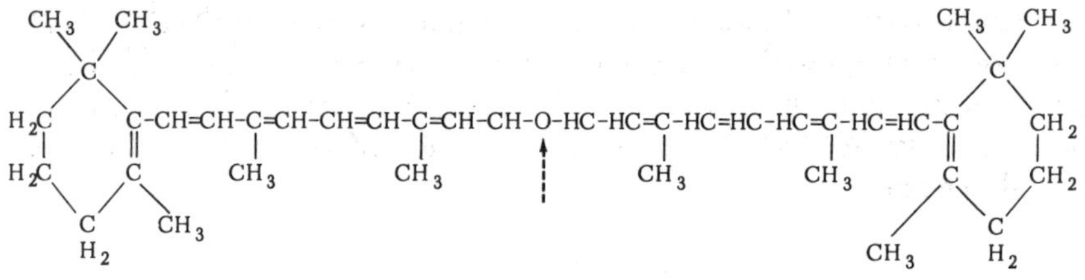

CH_3 CH_3

H_2C C-CH=CH-C=CH-CH=CH-C=CH-CH-O-HC-HC=C-HC=HC-HC=C-HC=HC-C CH_2
H_2C C CH_3 CH_3 CH_3 CH_3 CH_2
C CH_3
H_2

CH_3 CH_3
CH_3 H_2

beta–carotene

CH_3 CH_3

HO H_2C-HC=C-HC=HC-HC=C-HC=HC-C CH_2
CH_3 CH_3 CH_2
CH_3 H_2

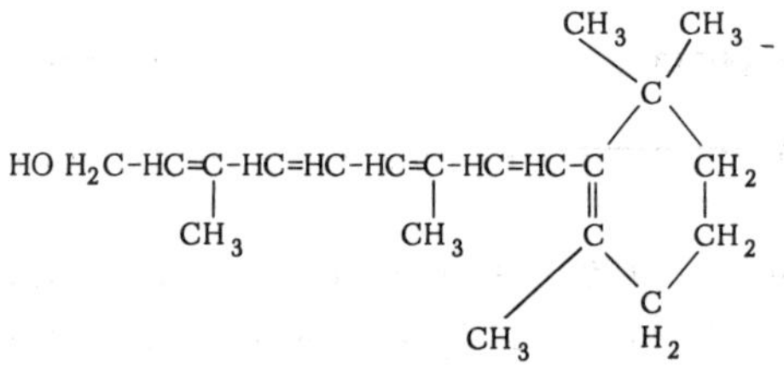

vitamin A_1

Amoeba and ciliated protozoa respond to light, generally moving away from an intense stimulus. Since there is no evidence for the presence of a photoreceptive pigment, these avoiding responses are taken as indication for the photosensitivity of protoplasm. The presence of pigments serving photoreception is limited mainly to the phyto-flagellates.

Euglena, a green flagellated protozoan, possess a red pigment granule, the *stigma,* in the anterior region and near the base of the flagellum. The region of the stigma and the flagellar base is recognized as a photoreceptive area. The animal's responses to light depend on the manner in which the stimulus falls on the stigma region. Attempts to identify the pigment have met with limited success and indications are that it contains a mixture of carotenoids.

Photoreceptive pigments are present in individual cells, clusters of cells or specialized visual organs in many of the invertebrates and in the eyes of vertebrates. While the materials have not been identified in all instances, there is sufficient evidence to indicate that they consist of a form of vitamin A in conjugation with a protein.

The pigment about which the most is known is *rhodopsin,* or visual purple which has been isolated from the rod cells of amphibian, some fish and mammalian eyes. If the eyes of these forms are removed in darkness the area of the receptor cells has a purple appearance, but on exposure to light the color changes through orange and yellow eventually to become colorless. These color changes are evidence for chemical reactions. Studies on the mechanisms have indicated that rhodopsin is composed of a combination of vitamin A_1 and a protein, *opsin,* which undergoes decomposition on exposure to light but in darkness is reconstituted within the eye according to the following general scheme:

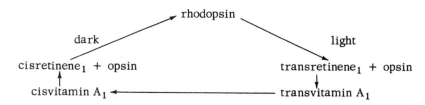

In the human eye the *rod cells* and rhodopsin are concerned with night vision without color appreciation. It is probable that rhodopsin plays a similar role in vision of animals that are thought to be color blind and whose eyes possess only rod cells from which rhodopsin has been identified. Color vision generally is ascribed to another type of receptor cell. Under normal conditions, photoreceptors show a rapid rate of adaptation in the presence of intense light. This would relate to the decomposition of rhodopsin so that in its comparative absence the stimulation effect would be diminished. On the other hand, if one has been in a darkened room for a period of time and then emerges into sunlight, the stimulus may be so intense as a result of the greater amount of rhodopsin which has been formed that there would be an uncomfortable glare until adaptation occurred again.

Rhodopsin is present in the eyes of terrestrial vertebrates, amphibians and marine invertebrates and fishes. Another photoreceptive pigment, *porphyropsin,* is present in the eyes of fresh water fishes. Porphyropsin is similar to rhodopsin except that it contains vitamin A_2 and on exposure to light breaks down into opsin and retinene$_2$; otherwise the cyclic changes in light and darkness are the same. An interesting observation in comparative biology is seen in the differing visual cycles in the developing frog. In the tadpole the eye contains porphyropsin, as does a fresh water fish. Following metamorphosis rhodopsin is found, also expected of the mature amphibian in adapting to a terrestrial form. Additional proof that the visual pigment relates to fresh water or marine environment is seen in the eye of fishes such as the salmon, which spawn in fresh water but live mostly at sea. The eye contains both rhodopsin and porphyropsin, the latter predominating. Eels, which spawn at sea but live mostly in fresh water, also have both pigments, but rhodopsin predominates. It appears that the condition under which life begins is of greater influence.

Cone cells act as receptors in those forms of life having color appreciation. It is interesting to note, however, that the frog, in which color vision is not necessarily recognized, possesses cone cells in its eye. A pigment, *iodopsin,* has been isolated from these cells, and it may serve as the photoreceptive material. It should be obvious that a single pigment would be unlikely to serve in color appreciation since all photostimulation would be in the range of its maximum light absorption and different wave lengths could not be stimulatory to separate receptor cells.

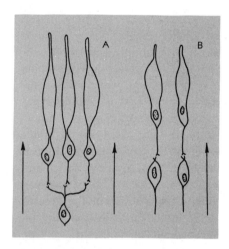

Fig. 22. Rod cells (A) and cone cells (B) of the vertebrate eye. Light reaches the receptors in the direction indicated by the arrows. Impulses are carried from the receptors by neurons.

Difficulty in isolation of different types of pigments from cone cells may be due to their low concentration, which escapes detection. A theory of long standing, the Young-Helmholtz theory of color vision, proposes the presence of three types of cone cells, each containing a specific pigment. One of these absorbs light maximally at about 410 mu and is concerned with violet vision. Another cone contains a pigment whose maximum light absorption is at 510 mu and serves sensation of green color vision. The third accounts for red vision and absorbs light at 685 mu (Figure 21). Again it must be remembered that the conscious sensation depends on brain interpretation of incoming nerve impulses. Light of other wave lengths might furnish a lesser stimulation to two receptors, and this would result in sensation of orange at 650 mu as incoming impulses from red and green-perceiving cones reach the brain, and blue at 450 mu as other receptors were stimulated to varying degrees.

Studies employing microelectrodes placed in contact with single cone cells of the retina have identified three types of cells responding maximally to light at wave lengths of 445, 535 and 570 mu, respectively. Although one light wave length for maximum stimulation is not in agreement with the earlier theory, the evidence seems generally related to the Young-Helmholtz theory to the extent that it suffices for an introductory understanding.

Besides the differences of receptor pigment in the eyes of different animals, interesting variations in the types of receptor cells present in vertebrate eyes seem related to the animal's behavior. The owl, a nocturnal bird, has an eye which contains mainly rod cells. Because of this the owl is capable of moving about in the dark but is blinded by the intense photostimulation of daylight. On the other hand, the chicken eye contains mainly cone cells and as such would be expected to be active during daylight hours but unable to see in the dark.

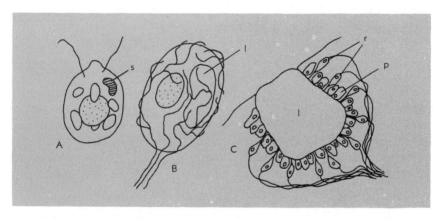

Fig. 23. Simple visual sense organs: A. Chlamydomonas with lens-shaped body to focus light on the stigma (s). B. The one-celled epithelial photoreceptor in the earthworm covered by a network of neuron endings and containing a lens structure (l). (C) The ocellus of an anemone showing the lens (l), pigment cells (p) and receptor cells (r).

It should be obvious from the previous discussion that photoreceptive pigments, regardless of whether they are based on a composition built around a form of vitamin A or one of the carotenoids, would serve in the same basic manner. Light is absorbed and the energy thus derived evokes a chemical change resulting in the development of generator potentials. As one considers the variety of visual sense organs in animals, it must be kept in mind that this basic function of light absorption is served by all photoreceptive cells. Differences in organ structure serve, for the most part, the concentration or focusing of light on the particular region of the receptor cells for best stimulation.

The simplest type of focusing mechanism is found in flagellated protozoa such as *Chlamydomonas*. The very curvature of the cell surface tends to concentrate the light on the stigma. Even within the metazoa single cells may act as photoreceptors and in the earthworm a lenslike cytoplasmic structure concentrates the light for more effective stimulation. Most of these receptors are concentrated in the anterior segments and account for that animal's positive phototaxis in dim illumination. Light sensitivity is general over the entire surface of echinoderms and is probably related to single-cell receptors. The same situation occurs in coelenterates, although in some of these the *ocellus*, or light sensitive organ is a multicellular structure with a lens for light concentration on the receptor cells.

With the development of the more complex ocellus there is a greater ability to discern light direction and to orient movement according to its source. Planaria displays phototropic responses as a result of its two anterior eye structures. Each of these lies closely beneath the surface. The epithelial cells above the eyes are not pigmented as they are in other portions of the body, thus it is possible that light may penetrate to stimulate the receptor cells. Light is not equally effective from all directions, however, for the receptors are protected, except anteriolaterally, by their inclusion within a cup of pigmented cells. Planaria

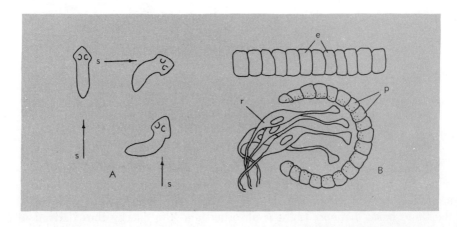

Fig. 24. The eye of Planaria: A. Entire animal, showing responses to illumination from different directional sources (s). B. Detail of eye structure: epithelium (e), pigment cells (p), receptor cell (r).

will normally orient itself to move away from the light, and the presence of two eyes contributes to the animal's ability to respond quickly and accurately to changes in light source. If the eyes are removed from Planaria, movements are more random, but the animals will eventually concentrate in darker regions, indicating that generalized epithelial receptors also are present.

As the eye structure becomes larger and contains more photoreceptive cells, there is offered the opportunity for better orientation and also the recognition of patterns within the visual field. The eye of the mollusk, nautilus, has a small opening at the front through which light may enter. The receptors are protected from all other directions by surrounding pigment cells. This eye functions like a simple pinhole

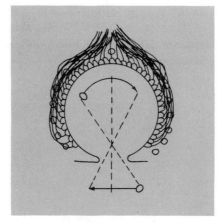

Fig. 25. The eye of nautilus showing manner of field stimulation to the receptor area.

camera in that the image is inverted. The many receptors, which may be differentially stimulated by light of varying intensity from the visual field, might respond with impulse discharge according to the strength of the stimulus. In some respects, this eye is very similar to that of the vertebrates. A notable difference is that some receptor cells discharge impulses on discontinuation of the light stimulus. This further enables the animal to discern differences in light intensity. Similar receptors are found in the eye of certain insects and the frog.

Insects possess both simple and compound eyes. The basic photoreceptive structures are similar in both. In the simple eye several of these lie beneath a single lens and are not likely to receive distinct stimuli. The compound eye is peculiar in that lens, and receptor structures are repeated many times as separate units, thus increasing sensitivity to varying degrees of illumination and even to patterns in the visual field.

In either type of eye a distinct system is present for focusing the light on the receptor cells. The clear *cornea* is of cuticular origin. Lying beneath it is the *crystalline body* formed by secretory cells. These two structures focus the light on the *rhabdom,* a rod of highly refractile material which conducts the light along its length. In the compound eye a *basement membrane* acts as a reflecting surface so the light re-traverses the rhabdom. It is thought that the light causes chemical changes in the rhabdom and that the products are responsible for stimulation of the sensory cells. In the optimum simple eye arrangement areas of light and dark may be perceived, but image formation is not possible. Nevertheless, insects with several simple eyes, such as the spider and certain larvae, may detect relative distance of objects as a result of their different overlapping visual angles.

The compound eye varies from the simple eye in that each visual unit containing a rhabdom has its own lens system. As a rule, each rhabdom is surrounded by seven sensory cells. *Iris cells* are heavily

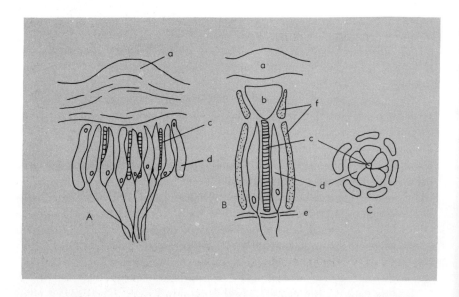

Fig. 26. Representative arthropod eyes: A. Simple eye, like a spider. B. Unit of compound eye. C. Cross section of B: cuticular cornea (a), crystalline body (b), rhabdom (c), receptor cell (d), basement membrane (e), pigmented iris cells (f).

pigmented and limit incoming light to the visual unit, or *ommatidium.* In some types of compound eyes, pigment may move outward or backward, depending on the intensity of illumination, so that in effect the eye may become light or dark adapted. Mosaic vision results in the compound eye, which contains thousands of ommatidia. It should be obvious that this type of eye would be most effective in the instance of a moving object which would result in a series of changing visual stimuli to the ommatidia. In the crustacea vision is improved by the location of the compound eyes on the tips of stalks which may be waved, thus creating a better visual sense with movement.

In many respects, the eye of the squid and vertebrates is similar to the simple eye of the arthropods in that a single lens system focuses light on all the receptors. Most of the light refraction is accomplished by the *cornea.* The *lens* is for the purpose of fine adjustment of vision in viewing objects at different distances. Light enters the eye from the front through the *pupil* aperture of the *iris.* Light coming from directly ahead falls behind the lens on an area of the retina called the *fovea,* but that entering at an angle falls on the more peripheral portions of the retina.

The *retina* is that layer of the eyeball which contains the photoreceptor cells, that is, the rods and cones. They are not equally distributed in all areas. The *optic nerve,* made up of neurons from all receptor cells of the retina, represents an area where no receptors are found; more specifically, that area is referred to as the *optic disc.* Since there are no receptors in the optic disc, light falling on that point will not be perceived. For that reason, it is recognized as the blind spot. Cone cells are present in greatest number per unit area in the fovea, actually being packed in so tightly that when viewed microscopically from the surface they appear hexagonal. The greater concentration of cone cells accounts for this region of the eye being the most sensitive for color vision in bright light. Peripheral portions of the retina possess fewer cone cells, so color vision acuity diminishes in those areas. Rod cells, on the other hand, are absent from the fovea but are found in the peripheral regions. This explains one's being able to see objects more distinctly at night if one is looking slightly to the side, for then the light from the object falls in the peripheral region where rod cells are present for vision in dim illumination.

It was mentioned earlier that adaptation occurs quickly in photoreceptors. In the vertebrate eye this adaptation is offset by eyeball movements which are not detectable in vision but which result in slight variations in the pattern of photostimulation to the retinal receptor cells. In this regard, the vertebrate eye, like the compound eye of the arthro-

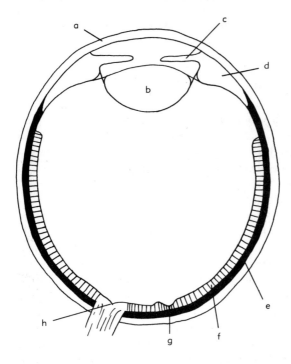

Fig. 27. The vertebrate eye as seen from above: cornea (a), lens (b), iris (c), ciliary body with suspensory ligaments supporting the lens, (d), pigmented choroid (e), retina (f), fovea (g), optic disc and nerve (h).

pod, functions better in the presence of motion. In either instance, however, it is important that the movements are not too fast, for this would result in failure of an adequate stimulation to occur, regardless of the light intensity.

Space perception with a single functional eye is mainly dependent on relative size of objects. In man and other primates an additional advantage is furnished in space perception in that both eyes are directed forward so the visual fields overlap. A three-dimensional object held directly in front of the eyes is seen differently by each eye: the right eye seeing more of the right side of the object, the left eye obtaining the left-hand view. These views will furnish different retinal stimuli, and the resulting impulses are interpreted in the brain to give a three-dimensional effect. So that light from the object being directly viewed falls on the fovea of both retinae, it is extremely important that both eyes be properly positioned by the muscles which move them. If this occurs, light from all other regions of the visual fields also falls on appropriate points of the retina, referred to for any single object as *corresponding points*. The importance of proper positioning of the eyes may be demonstrated by pushing lightly on the side of one eyeball with the finger. This displaces the eye so that corresponding points are not stimulated and double vision results.

ADDITIONAL READING

KENNEDY, DONALD, *Photophysiology* Vol. 2, Arthur C. Giese (ed.), New York: Academic Press Inc., 1964, pp. 79-121.

MacNICHOL, EDWARD F., JR., "Three-Pigment Color Vision," *Scientific American* 211:48-56, 1964.

CHAPTER 8

The nervous system

A nervous system serves the general purpose of coordinating an animal's actions so they are in agreement with environmental conditions. Most behavior is dependent on reflex action, that is, reaction to a stimulus. In the simplest sense this is seen in a single cell responding to some presented condition, as an amoeba moving toward and engulfing a food organism or a ciliate moving away from the region of a harmful chemical; however, complicated as reactions may be at the molecular and organelle level, reflexes are usually considered to be more complex since several cellular components will eventually be involved in the chain of events leading to a reflex action.

The cellular components which contribute to reflex action, from the point of stimulation to the eventual response, make up a *reflex arc.* The first of these components is the *receptor,* which is stimulated by some specific environmental event or condition. From this point, the impulse must be conducted to other portions of the body in order to bring about a response. This conduction is effected through neurons which are of at least two types. The first type conducts the impulse toward the animal's nervous system and is the *afferent,* or *sensory neuron.* The second type, the *efferent,* or *motor neuron* carries the impulse from the nervous system out to some region of the body where a response is evoked in an *effector* structure. The effector may be a muscle cell which by its contraction causes movement of a part or a glandular cell which releases its particular secretion. By the involvement of these four components a reflex action is made possible.

A fifth component or series of components may also be present: the *association neuron(s)* which transmit impulses between the afferent and efferent neurons. Association neurons may be present in large numbers, and it is through their multiple branches that impulses may spread from one afferent pathway into several efferent channels and eventually activate a large number of effectors. Much of the mass of a nervous system is composed of association neurons through which many portions of the body are related to one another. Differences in synaptic resistance through association neurons will dictate the extent to which facilitation will be required in order that impulses may be transmitted into final efferent pathways. For this reason, the degree to which an animal responds may vary directly with the intensity of the stimulating force. It is due to the reduction of synaptic resistance in these regions that strychnine causes convulsive action.

The behavior of invertebrates is mainly dependent on reflex action without voluntary or conscious involvement. Reflexes of the lower animals are mainly of the *unconditioned* or inborn type; that is, they occur without the animal's previous exposure to the conditions leading to the response. Such reactions are commonly referred to as *instincts*. They depend on well-established pathways through which impulses will travel and account for behavior such as food getting, nest building, locomotion or production of particular types of sounds. Instinctive behavior may give the impression of intelligence, especially in such forms as ants and bees which have colonial habits. This is indication of the complex nature of the pathways.

In contrast to these responses are *conditioned reflexes* which result from repeatedly occurring experiences. Most of the behavior of man and higher vertebrates depends on conditioned reflexes which are actually an indication of a learning process. The greater the number of conditioned responses an animal shows, the more complex will be its behavior. This will, of course, require a more complex nervous system in order to accommodate the greater number of impulse pathways which must be involved.

Consciousness of environmental conditions is indicated in mammals and especially in developed primates. The ability to interpret an impulse arising from some receptor as it reaches a specialized portion of the nervous system allows for the finest appreciation of surrounding conditions. Specific regions of the brain have been identified as having interpretive roles relating to cutaneous, visual, gustatory, olfactory and auditory sensations. As these functions become related to conditioned reflexes the potential emerges for the voluntary performance of purposeful acts. The refinement of this ability is identified with intelligence, for which the most highly developed nervous system is required. In the following pages, various types of nervous systems will be considered to illustrate the basic principles involved which eventually lead to this highest state of coordinative capacity.

THE NERVE NET

This system has been mentioned previously (page 10) as one composed of protoneurons over which impulses may pass in any direction. Smaller cells with cilia-like extensions from their terminal endings serve as receptors for mechanical, thermal and chemical stimuli. The protoneurons carry impulses at a rate of about 10 cm. per second to muscle cells and cnidoblasts, resulting in contraction and nematocyst discharge.

Stimulation in any region results in contraction, and if the stimulus is sufficiently strong the whole animal will contract sharply. This indicates a limited capacity for gradation of response even in this simple system. There is also evidence that some directional control exists. In order to cause contraction, a stronger stimulus must be applied to Hydra at the tip of a tentacle than at a more central location, and a severed portion of tentacle will be relaxed while contraction occurs in the area of the animal immediately adjacent to the cut.

A certain degree of coordinated activity is apparent in Hydra. Food organisms which have been captured as a result of nematocyst discharge are directed toward the mouth by the tentacles. Furthermore, the animal is capable of moving from one place to another by bending over, temporarily attaching its tentacles to the substrate and somersaulting to a new location. Such behavior in these primitive forms indicates the early appearance of a system which may eventually furnish the means for coordination of more complex nature.

NERVE RING STRUCTURES

Among the medusoid coelenterates, such as aurelia, a nerve net is also present, but the protoneurons are especially concentrated in a ring at the outer margin of the bell, generally following the ring canal of the gastrovascular system. Radial concentrations of protoneurons also follow the four radial canals toward the mouth region, and smaller branches extend inward from the nerve ring. Although these protoneuron concentrations are different from the nerve structures of higher forms, in which neuron extensions lie close together and even may be enclosed in a connective tissue sheath, they represent the beginnings of such structures. Another interesting occurrence, first seen in these forms, is the massing of protoneurons to furnish enlargements about the circumference of the nerve ring. Such a mass of protoneurons, or

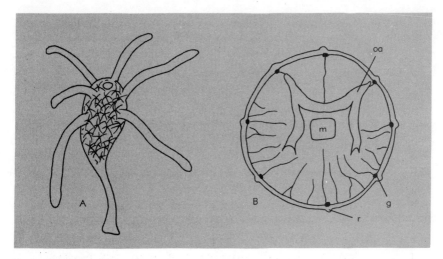

Fig. 28. A. Hydra showing a portion of the nerve net system. B. Diagrammatic view of a medusoid; ventral view with two oral arms removed to show radial concentrations of protoneurons leading to nerve ring. Rhopalium (r), ganglion (g), mouth (m), oral arm (oa).

neurons in higher forms, is referred to as a *ganglion*. A ganglion is found in close association with each of the eight sensory organs, or *rhopalia* at the margin of the bell. The rhopalia contain receptor cells, some of which serve the sense of equilibrium while others act as photoreceptors. That these rhopalia are of significance in swimming movement is seen in animals from which most have been removed; contractions of the bell originate from the remaining rhopalia.

The close association of the nerve ring and its ganglia with the rhopalia allows for coordinated swimming. It has been shown that conduction is much faster in the ring than through a generalized nerve net, impulses being transmitted at rates up to 25 cm. per second. If the margin is removed as a continuous ring from the rest of the body, the application of a stimulus will initiate impulses which continue in a circular fashion for several hours without diminished rate or intensity.

A somewhat similar structure is seen in the echinoderms and is well represented in the starfish. A ring of nerve tissue surrounds the mouth. From this ring radial nerves extend outward through each arm. Ganglia may be identified at various locations on the ring and radial nerves. Although a nerve net extends from these ganglia, the ring and radial nerves exert a predominating control over the animal's behavior. While a severed arm shows coordinated movement of its tube feet, so that

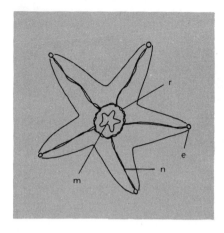

Fig. 29. Ventral view of starfish indicating location of nerve ring (r) surrounding the mouth (m) and the radial nerves (n) extending to pigmented eyespots (e).

independent locomotion may still occur, the ring is of major importance. If it is sectioned or removed, righting movements are impaired or completely lost in the otherwise intact animal. In spite of the apparent simplicity of the nervous system in echinoderms and the persistence of a nerve net, it would appear that protoneuron associations have become more important in transmission control, for the presence of strychnine will result in disruption of movements that normally are well coordinated.

CEPHALIZATION

As animals develop in length through bilateral symmetry there is a tendency for one end to dominate over the rest of the body. That dominating end, the anterior, contains the greater concentration of receptors. These structures develop concurrently with a greater concentration of nerve tissue. The total of such development is referred to as cephalization.

The enlarged anterior ganglion, or brain is little more than a center for neurons leading from the sense organs and a reflex center through which impulses may travel to other portions of the body. In some instances, more than one ganglion may be present, each one concerned with a particular sense organ system.

A simple example of cephalization is seen in Planaria. There are two anterior ganglia into which neurons lead from the eyespots and mechanoreceptors and chemoreceptors in the lateral sensory lobes of the head. Extending backward from each ganglion is a nerve trunk from which nerve fibers branch off with some regularity. Groups of nerve fibers also connect the two trunks laterally, thus the reference to the planarian nervous system as a ladder system. There are no particular concentrations of nervous tissues at these points of cross connections or outward extensions so that the anterior ganglia retain a predominating control over the behavior of the entire animal. This control results from the ganglia, acting as a receiving center for impulses from receptors; however, if the anterior ganglia are removed the animal is still capable of coordinated movements and is sensitive to environmental changes as a result of receptors which are widely spread over the body. Much conduction to the muscular system is through a nerve net system which still plays a significant role.

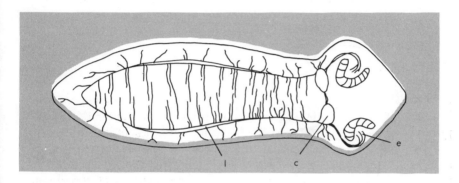

Fig. 30. The nervous system of Planaria: cephalic ganglion (c), lateral nerve (l), eyespot (e).

Even with this simple nervous system there is development of some conditioned reflexes. Planaria may be taught to perform in a maze, and some interesting experiments have indicated that this learning may in some way be RNA dependent. Animals from which the anterior ganglia have been removed must be retaught to perform, conditioning again being possible as the new ganglia are regenerated. Learning is impaired, however, if the regenerating portions are exposed to solutions of ribonuclease, an enzyme that breaks down RNA. On the other hand, extracts of "taught" planaria may actually hasten the learning process in regenerating portions.

The variation in general body form among the mollusks, from the clam to the squid, still allows for identification of anterior regions, and cephalization occurs with the development of the nervous system. Three types of ganglia are found in the clam. The paired anterior *cerebral ganglia* are connected by the *cerebral commissure*, a nerve trunk passing above the esophagus. Fibers extend from the cerebral ganglia to the anterior adductor muscle which is involved in shell closure. Two nerve trunks extend from each cerebral ganglion. One pair of these leads to the *pedal ganglia* which are concerned with movement of the foot muscle. A statocyst in that region may be involved in reflex actions occurring through the pedal ganglia. The second pair of nerve trunks extends posteriorly to the *visceral ganglia* which lie beneath the posterior adductor muscle and are connected by a small nerve branch. Covering the visceral ganglia is the *osphradium,* a mass of yellow epithelial cells which are thought to be sensitive to chemical substances in solution and of significance in testing the composition of water entering the mantle cavity.

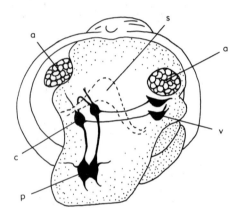

Fig. 31. The nervous system of the clam: cerebral ganglion (c), pedal ganglion (p), visceral ganglion (v), adductor muscles (a), stomach (s).

The extent to which cerebral ganglia dominate the others varies among the clams. In some forms their removal results in impaired foot movement, while in others the pedal ganglia seem to exert an independent control over the musculature. The adductor muscles seem under the direct control of their adjacent ganglia, both of which function independently in motor control; however, the cerebral ganglia may furnish inhibitory impulses to both muscles, and in the gastropods cerebral ganglion inhibition may extend into the foot muscles as well.

Molluscan nervous systems serve as excellent examples of the manner in which basic structures become concentrated in cephalization. In the squid, Loligo, the three pairs of ganglia become fused and form a brain about the esophagus. The *supraesophageal ganglion,* which is formed by the fused cerebral ganglia, has a general integrative control over the rest of the nervous system. It contains centers from which

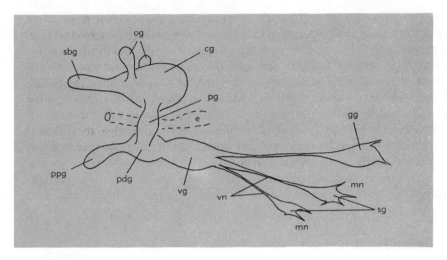

Fig. 32. Major structures of the squid nervous system: cerebral ganglion (cg), pleural ganglion (pg), visceral ganglion (vg), pedal ganglion (pdg), optic ganglion (og), suprabuccal ganglion (sbg), propedal ganglion (ppg), stellate ganglion (sg), gastric ganglion (gg), visceral nerve (vn), mantle nerve (mn), esophagus (e).

impulses are initiated to cause many muscular movements. Centers for olfactory and visual interpretation are also found here. The *optic lobes*, attached to the supraesophageal ganglion, represent nerve tracts from the retinae of the highly specialized eyes.

The pairs of pedal and visceral ganglia are fused and lie beneath the esophagus. Although they are separately distinguishable in Loligo, in some of the cephalopods there is further fusion to form a single *subesophageal ganglion*. The *pleural ganglia* resemble the nerve trunks in the clam, connecting the cerebral to the pedal ganglia. Minor ganglia, the *suprabuccal* and *propedal*, connect by nerve trunks to the cerebral and pedal ganglia, respectively.

Posterior to the visceral ganglion are the two *stellate* and single *gastric* ganglia. The *visceral nerve* contains giant axons which extend from cell bodies in the cerebral ganglion out through the stellate ganglion to innervate the muscles of the mantle. The larger of these fibers, which conduct more rapidly, extend to the most pheripheral regions, while smaller and more slowly conducting neurons connect to muscle cells located closer to the stellate ganglia.

The subesophageal portion of the brain contains centers for respiratory movements and control of tentacles, funnel and eye muscles. In the octopus a *pupil-constricting center* is found in this region.

The brain of the cephalopod represents a remarkable progression to allow quite complex behavior. While actions such as ink-sac contraction and chromatophore changes may be attributed to inborn reflexes, the octopus displays a remarkable capacity for developing conditioned responses. The eye of the octopus, as well as that of the squid, is capable of pattern and size recognition. Although an octopus may attack smaller moving objects, as a rule, larger ones will be avoided. By furnishing differently shaped smaller objects and applying an electrical shock when certain ones are approached, it has been possible to teach the octopus to avoid those objects whose shapes are related to the shock. Similar learning processes have been demonstrated by the use of objects with different types of surfaces, thereby demonstrating fine discrimination in the sense of touch.

SEGMENTATION

Segmental development in an animal allows for the repetition of basic units of organization along its length. Differentiation within the segments accounts for specific morphological appearance and peculiar functional capacities. Segmentation is apparent in the earthworm but little variation in individual segments is present. In the crustaceans and insects segmental specialization accounts for great differences in external appearance. The segmental organization in the fish is seen in the muscular structures, although this is not apparent in the external body form. In higher vertebrates and especially in the primates, there is very little gross evidence for segmental organization, but its presence is significant in the nervous system.

It is within the nervous system during its development as well as in the final body form that segmentation is especially obvious and important for animal function. Although a brain structure is present, the posterior units of organization are responsible for a certain degree of independence within each segment. In higher forms the brain assumes a greater dominance in determining the total behavior.

The nervous system of the earthworm displays both the simple beginnings of cephalization and segmentation as well. The brain consists of two *suprapharyngeal ganglia* in the third segment with a short connecting commissure. Neurons from the prostomium, where sensory organs are present in large numbers, lead into these ganglia. Circumpharyngeal connectives lead lateroposteriorly to connect to the paired but closely fused *subpharyngeal ganglia* in the fourth segment. From this point the *ventral nerve cord* extends posteriorly with an enlargement or segmental ganglion (actually two ganglia closely fused as is the subpharyngeal ganglion) located in each segment. From each ganglion three pairs of nerves extend ventrolaterally. These nerves are composed of the fiber extensions of sensory and motor neurons. Sensory neurons carry impulses into the cord from the different types of receptors that are distributed over the body surface. Within the ganglion these fibers synapse with motor neurons whose axons carry impulses out through segmental nerves to the muscles of the body wall. These components are readily recognizable as forming a reflex arc. Association neurons may also be present and establish connection within the cord between sensory and motor pathways of different segments. Giant fibers are also present and extend the entire length of the cord. Their origins are in the suprapharyngeal ganglia. Conduction in this fiber system is more rapid (about 1.5 m per second) than in other neurons and is

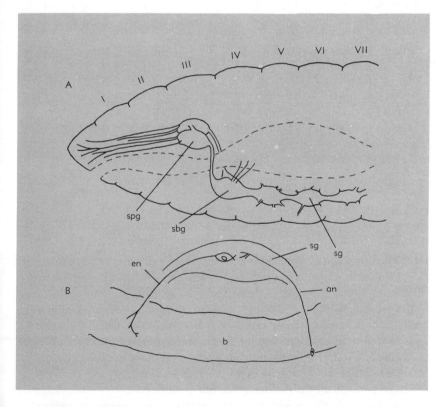

Fig. 33. The nervous system of the earthworm: A. Gross structure. B. Cross section through a segmental ganglion. Suprapharyngeal ganglion (spg), subpharyngeal ganglion (sbg), segmental ganglion (sg), afferent neuron (an), efferent neuron (en), body wall (b).

probably responsible for the normal, backward-progressing contractions essential for movement.

The suprapharyngeal ganglia function mainly as relay centers for impulses coming from sense organs. These impulses, in their posterior transmission, bring about coordination of the total animal. Isolated segments of the earthworm are capable of reflex responses, and sections containing several segments display locomotor activity. Fibers from the subpharyngeal ganglia lead to the anterior portions of the gut.

The earthworm, like the planaria flatworm, may be taught by the application of stimuli to move through a maze in a particular manner. This type of conditioned reflex is lost on removal of anterior segments containing the brain. In the event that anterior regeneration occurs with formation of a new brain, conditioning again is possible, but the animal must be retrained. Thus, even with a brain serving mainly as a relay center, there are developed nerve pathways of sufficient complexity to allow the development of preferential directions of conduction.

Segmentation is obvious in the external structure of the arthropods. The nervous system is also developed along segmental lines and is remarkably similar to that of the annelids. In some respects, it is more primitive, for the nerve trunks which extend through the body remain paired rather than fusing like the ganglia. In the simplest arthropods and in the millipedes and centipedes the segmental ganglia are of equal size and distribution throughout the length of the body. With specialization of the appendages the ganglia become enlarged in proportion to the complexity of the structures which its nerves must serve, and in some of the insects the segmental ganglia become fused into a single structure. Nerves of the segmental ganglia carry both afferent and efferent neurons, serving reflex actions as they do in the annelids.

The basic structure of the brain is also remarkably similar to that of the annelids. It consists of a supraesophageal ganglion which lies dorsal to the alimentary tract and is connected laterally by the esophageal tracts to the subesophageal ganglion, formed by fusion of ganglia associated with the mouth parts. From these basic ganglia there may be derived specialized lobes associated with structures in the head region. Generally, the lobes receiving neurons from the sense organs are the largest. Differences in the sizes of lobes in different arthropods are generally related to the importance of those organs to the animal's behavior. Organs for vision may consist of approximately one per cent of the brain mass in those forms having simple eyes or more than fifty per cent in those with large compound eyes. Olfactory centers are much larger in nocturnal insects where vision plays a less important role in determining behavior.

The subesophageal ganglion contains nerve cell bodies whose motor impulses are transmitted to the mouth parts. While it does not appear to be a center for coordination of movement initiated through the segmental nerves (it can be removed and normal locomotion can still occur), it apparently does perform a faciliatory control over segmental reflexes. Insects from which the structure has been removed are still capable of movement and, in fact, locomotion is exaggerated.

The supraesophageal ganglion is mainly a receiving center for impulses coming from the sense organs in the head region and relaying their transmission to other regions of the body for reflex actions. This portion of the nervous system also exerts a control over muscle tone or tension. If one side is damaged or removed, the muscles on that side of the body show less contractile force so the body may be bent in the opposite direction by the stronger contractions on the opposite side. Such an insect may even be caused to walk in circles in the direction of the normal portion of the brain.

An excellent example of specialization is seen in the structure of the brain of the bee (Figure 34). The *optic lobes,* which contain sensory fibers from the compound eyes, comprise a great portion of the brain. From this it would be expected that visual stimuli play a major role in the bee's behavior. The antennal nerve carries afferent impulses from

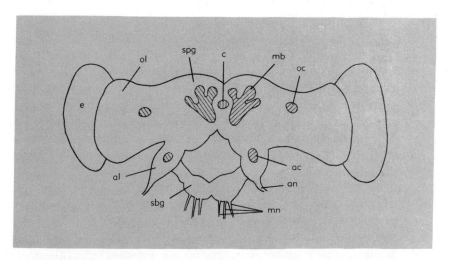

Fig. 34. Anterior view of the brain of the bee: Internal structures are shaded; supraesophageal ganglion (spg), optic lobe (ol), compound eye (e), antennule lobe (al), subesophageal ganglion (sbg), antennule nerve (an), nerves to mouth parts (mn), mushroom body (mb), central body (c), optic center (oc), antennule center (ac).

its various receptors into the *antennal lobe*. Motor neurons from the subesophageal ganglia innervate the various mouth parts.

Within the brain a number of centers may be identified. The *mushroom body* is the most important of these and is especially obvious in the brain of the bee. It contains the cell bodies of a great number of sensory and motor neurons and probably is a center for reflexes of extreme complexity which play an important role in social behavior.

Conditioned reflexes, which may be established in insects, indicate a great capacity for the alteration of behavior in order best to cope with environmental changes. Insects may be taught to perform in a maze or to seek areas of considerable illumination, although having a normal tendency to remain in the dark. Bees recognize differences in simple pattern figures and may be taught to react to these, depending on the nature of the stimulus furnished concurrently with the figure presentation.

Unconditioned reflexes are extremely important in colonial behavior of insects and indicate the extent to which particular neuronal pathways are essential for their way of life. It is generally accepted that bees in a colony are capable through their movements of communicating to one another information regarding the direction, distance and relative quantity of food.

THE VERTEBRATE NERVOUS SYSTEM

The vertebrate nervous system is an excellent example of development along segmental lines and with cephalic domination. The segmental plan is obvious in the nerves which arise from the spinal cord, but the brain, especially that of the highest primates, furnishes an outward appearance which conceals its linear arrangement. An examination of the brain's development will reveal its linear segmental plan.

The vertebrate nervous system is of ectodermal origin. Very early in development there is a longitudinal invagination along the dorsal surface. Infolding continues until an ectodermal tube has been pinched off to lie beneath the surface of the dorsal body wall. This hollow tube persists, the cavity later being recognized as the central canal of the spinal cord and the ventricles of the brain. Very early in development there is an enlargement at the anterior end, the *encephalon*, from which the various portions of the brain will eventually be formed. The posterior hollow tube will become the *spinal cord*. This is the most primitive portion of the vertebrate nervous system, and one finds the simplest types of reflex functions, mainly of a protective nature, carried on by that level.

In its earliest stage the encephalon is little more than an anterior ganglion such as seen in the invertebrates. With continued development, segmentation gives rise to the forerunners of later and more easily recognized portions of the brain. There first appear three segments. Of these the middle one, the *mesencephalon,* is of immediate importance. While the anterior and posterior segments will again divide, this one remains as such and is eventually identified as the *midbrain.* For this reason, the midbrain is the center of some of the more primitive functions of the brain.

The posterior segment undergoes another division, giving rise to the *myelencephalon* and the *metencephalon.* The first of these will become the *medulla,* the lowest portion of the brain, while the metencephalon will differentiate into the *pons* and the *cerebellum.* The segment in front of the mesencephalon will divide again to give the *diencephalon,* from which the *thalami* and *hypothalamus* are derived as well as the posterior pituitary gland. The *telencephalon* develops into the *cerebrum,* the most anterior and the largest portion of the fully developed brain.

As the brain continues to develop certain portions become considerably enlarged so the linear structure cannot be strictly maintained within the confinement of the skull. The flexures of the brain allow for continued development within this spatial limitation (Figure 35), and as the telencephalon becomes greatly enlarged it actually covers more posterior segments. Nevertheless, the linear relation persists and represents the means of neural association between the higher and lower portions of the nervous system.

From the development of the nervous system it should be apparent that the posterior portions will be concerned with simple, protective reflexes and functions essential for the maintenance of life. More anterior segments of the brain refine body conditions and behavior, and the foremost portion eventually assumes a role of governing intelligent behavior.

The spinal cord is mainly a pathway through which impulses may be carried in ascending or descending directions through the nervous system, or at a given level from receptors to muscle or glandular structures for reflex activity. In man there are thirty-one pairs of *spinal nerves,* each of which is attached to the cord on the right and left sides by *dorsal* and *ventral roots.* A cross section of the spinal cord at the level of one of the pairs of spinal nerves is represented in Figure 36. The outer portion of the cord is composed of white matter and contains myelinated neuron extensions carrying impulses to higher or lower portions of the nervous system. It is through tracts of the white matter of the cord that motor impulses may be carried from the brain toward muscles and glands for their activation. Sensory impulses are carried through other tracts from receptors upward to the appropriate portion of the brain for interpretation as conscious sensation.

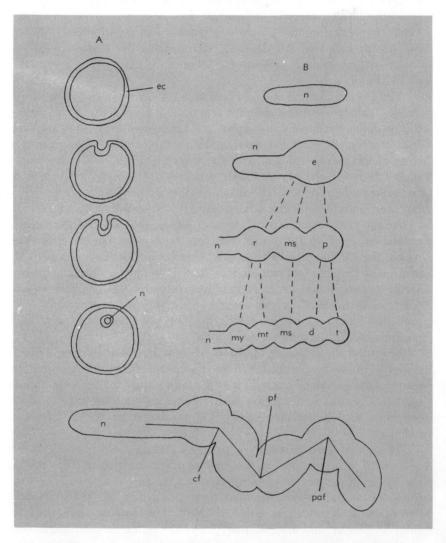

Fig. 35. Development of the vertebrate nervous system: A. Cross section to show formation of the neural tube by invagination of dorsal ectoderm. B. Longitudinal view to illustrate segmental plan of brain; ectoderm (ec), neural tube (n), encephalon (e), rhombencephalon (r), mesencephalon (ms), prosencephalon (p), myelencephalon (my), metencephalon (mt), diencephalon (d), telencephalon (t), cervical flexure (cf), pontine flexure (pf), parietal flexure (paf).

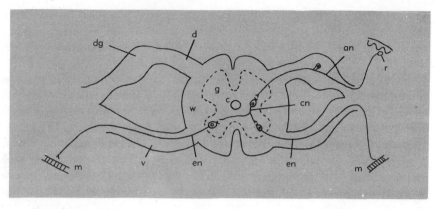

Fig. 36. Cross section of the spinal cord indicating components of a simple reflex arc: gray matter (g), white matter (w), central canal (c), dorsal root (d), dorsal root ganglion (dg), receptor in skin (r), afferent (sensory) neuron (an), association (central) neuron (cn), efferent (motor) neuron (en), muscle effector (m), ventral root (v).

Many reflex actions of the body are accomplished by nerve tracts through the spinal cord. The components necessary for the action, that is those of the reflex arc, are similar to those discussed earlier in relation to the annelid nervous system. Certain peculiarities in the higher form are worthy of mention. The cell bodies of the afferent neurons lie in a mass within the dorsal root and account for the enlargement in that region: the *dorsal root ganglion*.

In the afferent neuron the extension leading to the cell body is longer than the axon, and it is referred to as the *dendron*. The presence of association and efferent nerve cell bodies in the central portion of the cord accounts for the gray matter. Association neurons are of particular importance in the spreading of an impulse to the opposite side of the body and to higher or lower levels.

Spinal reflexes generally consist of limb flexion or extension (e.g., knee jerk) as a result of local stimulation. In some instances, the response may involve several muscle groups in directed movement, as is seen in the scratching reflex of the dog. Spinal reflex action is possible without the presence of higher portions of the nervous system and does not require conscious effort. It should be recognized that in the intact animal the impulses would also be carried to the brain for interpretation, but conscious sensation and effort would not be essential for the reflex to occur.

The medulla is the lowest portion of the brain and is concerned with the involuntary control of functions essential for the very maintenance of life. Respiratory movements, heart function, blood pressure and activities related to digestion are controlled by centers lying within the medulla. Damage to the medulla may cause impairment or loss of these vital functions with death as a result.

The pons and cerebellum, derived from the metencephalon, are mainly relay centers between higher and lower portions of the nervous system. In addition, the cerebellum acts to refine voluntary movements of body structures. These movements are initiated by impulses originating from higher areas of the brain, but if the cerebellum is destroyed coordination and muscular force are diminished. The cerebellum is also a reflex center for the adjustment of body posture and the maintenance of equilibrium resulting from the stimulation of proprioceptors of the muscles, tendons, joints and inner ear.

The midbrain, or mesencephalon consists primarily of white matter containing ascending and descending pathways through the brain. It is from the developmental and functional viewpoint the most primitive portion of the brain.

The thalami and hypothalamus, portions of the diencephalon, form the lateral walls and the floor, respectively, of the third ventricle of the brain. The ventricles are enlargements of the spinal cord's central canal as it continues into the brain. Three additional ventricles are present, one at approximately the level of the medulla and one in each of the two hemispheres of the cerebrum. The ventricles of the brain, the central canal of the spinal cord and the space surrounding the nervous system are all filled with the cerebrospinal fluid which has both a nutritive and cushioning function.

The hypothalamus is the functional area of most importance in the diencephalon. It contains centers controlling functions which are identified with and essential for higher types of life, for instance, body temperature, water balance, sleep and wakefulness. While damage to this portion of the brain might not lead to immediate loss of life, normal behavior would be greatly impaired, and death would eventually result from prolonged dysfunction.

The foremost segment of the brain, the telencephalon, develops into the cerebrum. This portion is greatly enlarged in higher forms and is concerned with the most advanced functions: voluntary action, conscious sensation and intelligent behavior. In enlargement of this segment the growth is greatest in the lateral aspects. This results in the formation of the right and left hemispheres of the cerebrum. As a general rule, the right hemisphere is concerned with motion and sensation on the left side of the body and vice versa. Commissural fibers connect the two hemispheres to effect appropriate coordination of the two sides.

The inner portion of the cerebrum consists of white matter and contains myelinated fibers. The outer portion, or *cortex* is gray matter and contains nerve cell bodies which are actually responsible for the initiation of conscious activity or interpretation of sensation. The cortex displays many *fissures* and convolutions, all of which add to the total surface available for nerve cell bodies. Some of these fissures are deeper than others and serve to set off particular areas or lobes of the cerebrum. These lobes are more than mere topographical areas, for particular types of functions are identified with each. The plotting of these areas has been made possible by observation of body movement following stimulation of a cortical area of the anesthetized animal or the recording of electrical activity in various portions of the brain following the application of a stimulus to a particular region of the body.

The *frontal lobe* is of particular importance in that it contains *motor areas* responsible for the initiation of conscious movement (Figure 37). The most lateral regions control muscle movements in

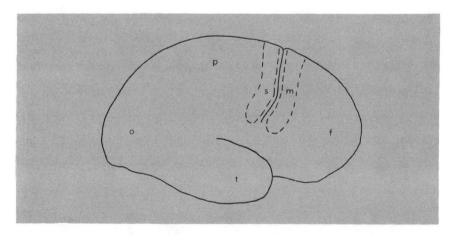

Fig. 37. Outline of the right cerebral hemisphere showing the frontal (f), parietal (p), occipital (o) and temporal (t) lobes and motor (m) and sensory (s) areas.

the facial and head region; progressing upward and centrally on the opposite side of the body are found arm, trunk, hip, leg and foot controls. Lying behind the frontal lobe and in the forward portion of the *parietal lobe* is the *somesthetic region* whose cells interpret incoming impulses originating from receptors over the body surface.

TABLE 2
The cranial nerves.

No.	Name	Motor Function and Organ Involved	Location of Motor Nucleus	Sensory Function and Organ Involved	Location of Sensory Area
1	Olfactory	-	-	smell, nose	temporal lobe
2	Optic	-	-	vision, retina	occipital lobe
3	Oculomotor	visual accommodation eyeball	midbrain	-	-
4	Trochlear	eyeball movement	midbrain	-	-
5	Trigeminal	chewing muscles	midbrain	pain, jaw and face	parietal lobe
6	Abducens	eyeball movement	pons	-	-
7	Facial	secretion of salivary glands	pons	taste, tongue	temporal lobe
8	Acoustic	muscles of face	frontal lobe	hearing, ear equilibrium, ear	temporal lobe cerebrum cerebellum spinal cord
9	Glossopharyngeal	secretion of salivary glands, swallowing, throat	medulla	taste, tongue	temporal lobe
10	Vagus	involuntary vital functions, viscera	medulla	involuntary vital functions, viscera	medulla
11	Accessory	shoulder movement	medulla	muscle sense, shoulders	medulla
12	Hypoglossal	movement, tongue	medulla	muscle sense, tongue	medulla

The same inversion is seen in the sensory as in the motor area so that the lower and more lateral portions are concerned with sensations in the higher portions of the body. The *occipital lobe* contains the *visuosensory area* which receives impulses from the retina of the eye and interprets these in vision. Sensations of taste, smell and hearing are interpreted by cells in the gray matter of the *temporal lobe.*

While many of the impulses into and from the brain may progress through the spinal cord and spinal nerves, certain of these are transmitted directly through nerves connective to the various portions of the brain itself, the *cranial nerves*. These nerves also exist in pairs, there being ten to twelve pairs in the true vertebrates. Nerves may be motor or sensory or both. Sensory nerves contain neurons whose impulses are carried into regions of the brain to serve in reflex function or to areas of the cerebral cortex for interpretation as conscious sensation. Motor nerves carry impulses outward from masses of nerve cell bodies called *nuclei* to effect a particular function. The cranial nerves are numbered in the order of their appearance from the ventral brain surface, proceeding backward; they are also given specific names that are generally suggestive of their major function. Some of the important information relative to the cranial nerves is given in Table 2.

It has been mentioned previously that as one examines in turn the portions of the nervous system in forward progression it is apparent there is a general tendency for the more anterior regions to be related to higher types of function. The basis for this type of function is furnished in the examination of the brains of different vertebrates as shown in Figure 38. In some of the lower forms particular regions of the brain show exaggerated development if the animal is dependent on a particular sense for its behavior. This is seen in the enlargement of the *optic lobes* (portions of the midbrain) and *olfactory lobes* (at the base of the cerebrum) where vision and the olfactory sense are of particular significance. This is suggestive of the unusual enlargement of particular portions of the insect brain.

The cerebrum is especially apparent by its enlargement in the higher forms and attains its greatest size in the primates and man, where conditioned reflexes play a greater role in the total pattern of behavior. It is also noted that in these forms there is a final tendency for enlargement of the most anterior portion of the cerebrum, the frontal lobes, which seems to parallel the capacity for intelligent action; however, indications are that intelligence in man is not related only to the frontal lobes. Loss of intelligent behavior following brain injury depends not so much on the specific area damaged but rather on the total extent of damage to all portions of the brain.

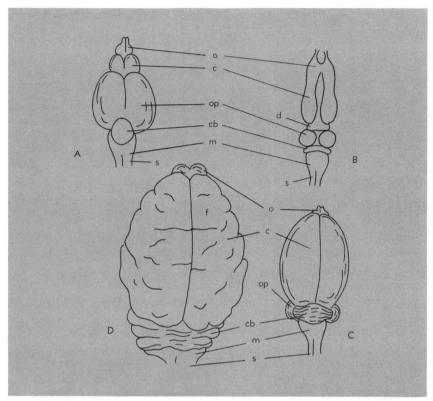

Fig. 38. Dorsal view of vertebrate brains: A. Fish; B. Frog; C. Bird; D. Mammal; olfactory lobe (o), cerebrum (c), optic lobe (op), diencephalon (d), cerebellum (cb), medulla (m), spinal cord (s), frontal lobe (f).

ADDITIONAL READING

BOYCOTT, BRYAN B., "Learning in the Octopus," *Scientific American* 212:42-50, 1965.

McCONNELL, JAMES V., "Memory Transfer through Cannibalism in Planarians," *Journal of Neuropsychiatry* 3:542-548, 1962.

ROEDER, KENNETH D., "Neural Mechanisms in Animal Behavior," *American Zoologist* 2:105-115, 1962.

VONFRISCH, KARL, "Dialects in the Language of the Bees," *Scientific American* 207:78-87, 1962.

CHAPTER 9

The nature
of hormones

In the previous chapters, consideration has been given to nervous factors involved in the coordination of an organism's activities. Even with the slow rate of conduction in nerve elements of primitive systems reactions occur with little delay following stimulation. Nervous coordination enables the animal to make immediate adjustments in its behavior in order to withstand, avoid or take advantage of changes in environmental conditions. The rapidity of the response makes it easier to appreciate nervous coordination in the study of animal behavior, but this is not the only available means for the adjustment of activities which contribute to the animal's total well-being.

A cell's activities depend on the total function of its organella, and these are influenced by conditions within the protoplasm. Cell function is also regulated by a variety of conditions in the immediate environment. Increasing temperature will increase the rate at which chemical reactions occur, and oxygen consumption will vary directly. Alteration of environmental pH has a great effect on the activity of enzymes which determine a cell's total metabolism. The relative availability of oxygen, and the presence of carbon dioxide, a waste product of respiration, also will influence cellular activity; however, these factors exert such a general control that almost all cells throughout the body will increase or decrease their metabolism. There is the further need that cells be called on under certain conditions to perform to a greater or lesser extent, the functions for which they have become specialized. More specific chemicals are required for such coordination; hormones serve in this capacity.

A *hormone* may be defined as a chemical substance produced by one cell, or type of cell which influences the activity of another cell or cell type. In order to be effective these chemical coordinators must be transported from the region of their formation to the other cells whose activities are to be controlled. This transfer may occur locally through the fluid immediately bathing the cell, or it may be effected through greater distances by means of a circulatory system. For this reason, the blood stream becomes an important factor in chemical control in larger animals. The responses to hormones are less obvious than are those of the nervous system so that they are not immediately detected; they may, however, be of much longer duration. They are especially concerned with the maintenance of a constant internal environment which is most favorable for normal tissue and organ functions.

Certain procedures are required in order to demonstrate the existence and action of a hormone. First, it is necessary to tentatively identify the cellular, tissue or organ source of the material. If dealing with a metazoan the suspected structure is then removed and the animal carefully observed for changes in its behavior or functional capacities. In many instances, this observation must be carefully continued over a prolonged period of time. If growth or differentiation are the functions involved, a considerable portion of the animal's life span will have passed before deficiencies are detectable. The third step is usually the most difficult of all. It involves the extraction of the active principle from the suspected structure and the return of that principle to the body in an effort to relieve the deficiency symptoms and to restore normal functions. (It is interesting to note that these basic procedures were established only slightly more than fifty years ago in conjunction with studies leading to the discovery of insulin.)

The chemical nature of the hormones and the fact that they exert their effect when in extremely low concentrations, account for the difficulty in isolating them in sufficient quantities for study. While some of the endocrine materials have a relatively low molecular weight and simple molecular structure others are much more complicated, being composed of a large number of amino acids in a polypeptide or simple protein structure. In some instances, it is proposed that waste products from one cell may have a regulatory effect on the metabolism of another. It may also occur that one is capable of synthesizing a particular nutrient in quantities excessive of those required so it is released to benefit another cell which requires the material but lacks the capacity for its synthesis. In this instance, the nutrient appears to function as a hormone.

Hormones may be classified into three categories according to their source: (1) cellular, (2) tissue and (3) glandular.

Cellular hormones are those produced by single cells, most notably protozoa and unicellular plants. Demonstration for the existence of such material is best given within a pure protozoan population, that is, one in which no other forms of life are present. The 'rate of growth and reproduction of individual cells increases within limitations as the number of cells present per unit volume of fluid medium is increased. If, on the other hand, the cellular population is excessively high, the rate of growth is diminished. The exact nature of such growth regulators has not been established, but there are indications that they may be relatively small molecules. One theory holds that a single substance is involved and that its effect is either stimulatory or inhibitory, depending on its relatively low or high concentration. Other evidence has been furnished for the existence of two separate materials, one of which is produced early and is stimulatory; the other, produced later, is specifically inhibitory. Regulatory factors also are involved in the growth of animal cells cultured *in vitro*. There also is recent evidence that during its growth, one species of protozoa may release materials either stimulatory or inhibitory to the growth of another species in the same fluid environment. The mechanism involved in these regulations of growth remain unexplained. It may be that the answer will relate to the most basic functions of cellular growth and reproduction.

Tissue hormones, as indicated by nomenclature, are produced in the metazoa. In these instances, the source displays a differentiated cellular organization but is not recognizable as a glandular structure. The neurohormones which have been discussed earlier—acetylcholine and epinephrine—are examples of tissue hormones. They are produced by nervous tissue and cause a change in the behavior; in muscle tissue, the change is by contraction; in the glandular tissue, by secretion. Serotonin, which has been mentioned as a possible factor in impulse mediation, is released from injured tissues and causes local capillary constriction.

A number of hormones produced by tissues of the digestive tract exert an influence over the release of digestive secretions by other cells, tissues or organs. Gastrin, pancreozymin and cholecystokinin all serve in this capacity.

Glandular hormones are the materials of most significance in chemical coordination of body functions. Glandular organs are of two types. One type releases its secretion through ducts, either into the alimentary tract or outside the body proper. The external secretions of these ducted, or *exocrine glands* are not involved in the control of the internal environment of the body. Such structures as the sweat, salivary and pancreatic glands are concerned with the excretion of wastes or secretion of digestive mixtures.

The glands to which this discussion is given are those that release their secretions into the blood stream. These ductless, or *endocrine glands* are the source of a large number of hormone substances which also are properly referred to as *endocrines*. The location of these endocrine glands is indicated in Figure 39, and their specific secretion products are listed in Table 3.

The functions of the endocrines, as briefly indicated in the table, appear to be quite complicated. It is probable, however, that their control is directed at specific reactions at the level of cellular metabolism. Although the endocrines do not function as enzymes, they do influence the action of enzymes, thus enabling cells to express their capabilities of specialization. The more apparent results are the gross changes in body reactions.

Some of the endocrines, *thyroxin* and *epinephrine,* most notably, have a pronounced effect on the rate at which oxygen is used in the

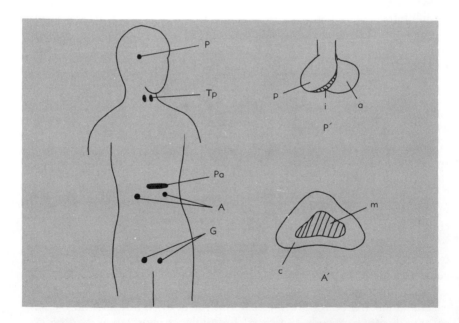

Fig. 39. The location of endocrine glands in the human body: P. Pituitary; P'. Detail of pituitary showing anterior (a), posterior (p) and intermediate (i) lobes; T_p Thyroids and parathyroids; Pa. pancreas; A. Adrenal; A'. Detail of adrenal showing cortex (c) and medulla (m); G. Gonads (testes and ovaries).

TABLE 3

The endocrine glands and their major secretions.

Gland and Endocrine	Controls
Pituitary, anterior lobe	
Somatotrophin (STH)	somatotrophic growth
Follicle-stimulating hormone (FSH)	reproductive cell development
Luteinizing hormone (LH, ICSH)	sex hormone formation
Luteotrophic hormone (LTH)	mammary gland
Thyrotrophic hormone (TSH)	thyroid secretion
Adrenocorticotrophic hormone (ACTH)	adrenal cortex secretion
Pituitary, posterior lobe	
Vasopressin	blood vessel constriction
Oxytocin	uterine contraction
Pituitary, intermediate lobe	
Intermedin	melanophore expansion
Thyroid	
Thyroxin	oxidation, differentiation in growth
Parathyroid	
Parathormone	calcium metabolism
Pancreas	
Insulin	glycogen storage, liver
Glucagon	glycogen breakdown, liver
Adrenal Cortex	
Corticosterone	antiinflammatory, spares carbohydrates
Deoxycorticosterone	Na and K balance
Adrenal medulla	
Epinephrine	oxidation, emergency responses
Norepinephrine	oxidation, emergency responses
Gonads, ovaries	
Estradiol	secondary sex characters
Progesterone	secondary sex characters
Gonads, testes	
Testosterone	secondary sex characters

animal's total metabolic activity. Epinephrine effects a greater rate of carbohydrate oxidation. This is accomplished by increasing the action of hexokinase, an enzyme essential for the phosphorylation of glucose, so there may follow a series of enzymatic reactions leading to the release of energy and the utilization of molecular oxygen. Through such action epinephrine causes an increased respiration, and the energy which is normally derived from cellular oxidation would result in greater muscle strength.

Thyroxin also increases oxygen consumption and over prolonged periods of time will cause considerable loss of body weight. The influence of thyroxin is exerted during the terminal stages of cellular oxidation. In the final enzymatic reactions which lead to the involvement of molecular oxygen several molecules of ATP are produced. The formation of ATP to some degree slows the rate at which the final enzymatic reactions are accomplished. Thyroxin uncouples the phosphorylating reactions, allowing the oxidative processes to be completed without the formation of ATP. Since most materials are oxidized through this final pathway, carbohydrates, lipids and amino acids are used at a more rapid rate. This accounts for the loss of body weight if the reactions are continued in excess. Such reactions would be wasteful in the total function of the body, but if properly controlled they serve a useful purpose in the body's total metabolism.

Since many chemicals are used in common by most living cells, it follows that those cells would possess similar enzymes. For this reason, it is not surprising to find that thyroxin and adrenalin have the expected effect on the metabolism when introduced artificially to lower forms of life. Although the thyroid and adrenal glands are lacking from the invertebrates, the enzyme systems for oxidation are present and it is these which are affected. It seems not unlikely that further recognition of this universality of action will occur as the true nature of hormonal control becomes better defined in future studies.

Under the influence of certain hormones the total protoplasmic mass may be increased or decreased. The effect may be accounted for by the influence on the cellular metabolism of amino acids. *Somatotrophin* (STH) from the anterior lobe of the pituitary has been shown to spare amino acids in cultures of cells grown *in vitro*. The lower rate at which amino acids are broken down for energy will result in cellular derivation of energy from other types of food materials, while amino acids are used in forming more protoplasm. *Corticosterone* from the adrenal cortex has the opposite effect. This hormone spares carbohydrates at the expense of greater amino acid utilization. The notable effect in the body is the reduction of the mass of certain tissues. Corticosterone's action in reducing the swelling around arthritic joints is probably due in part to the control by the hormone of enzymatically induced reactions within the cell. Corticosterone may even influence cellular metabolism to the extent that amino acids are converted to carbohydrates, thus resulting in a net increase in the total amount of the latter material available for the body's function.

Hormones from the pancreas control processes through which sugars from the blood are converted into glycogen, a carbohydrate storage product in the liver and muscle tissues. *Insulin* increases the rate of these reactions concerned with glycogen formation, especially in the liver. *Glucagon*, another hormone of the pancreas, causes the glycogen to break down to glucose. These two hormones will contribute to the proper balance of enzymatic reactions concerned with sugar storage for future use or its immediate availability to the body for energy.

Mineral metabolism is influenced by several of the hormones. The liberation of ACh from its bound form occurs simulanteously with changes in nerve cell membrane permeability to sodium ions and depolarization. The appearance of other ions in greater or lesser quantities in various portions of the body is under the influence of other hormones. *Parathormone* from the parathyroid glands controls reactions responsible for the deposition of calcium in skeletal structures. In some instances, ions are transported through cells or tissue membranes from one region of the body to another. These processes frequently occur in such a manner that passage is against a gradient, for materials are moved from the region of their lesser concentration into one of higher concentration. Such passage will involve expenditure of energy for which enzyme systems are essential. Within the kidney reactions of this type account for proper sodium and potassium balances in the body and are influenced in part by *deoxycorticosterone* and other hormones from the adrenal cortex. The enzyme systems responsible for these transfers are not known, but the reactions, which must occur at the cellular level, furnish another example of the nature of hormone involvement in coordinative function.

The more apparent responses through which coordination is recognized depends on these basic functions much in the same manner that nervous coordination depends on the functioning of neurons. Since much remains unresolved regarding the chemical reactions, our treatment of hormonal coordinating mechanism rests mainly with grossly apparent effects. In many instances, one must consider the abnormal situation following glandular removal or resulting from its pathological dysfunction in order to gain appreciation of the manner in which hormones control body function. Such situations will be cited since they are essential in the following discussion.

Additional Reading

Jenkin, Penelope M., *Animal Hormones—A Comparative Survey*, New York: Pergamon Press, Inc., 1962, pp. 1-15.

CHAPTER 10

Hormones
in coordination

The endocrine glands of the vertebrates are associated with many functions which are considered normal and even essential for life. The field of *endocrinology* deals with all the actions which possibly may be influenced by their secretions. Abnormal secretions may result in a variety of symptoms which, although undoubtedly relating to some basic change in cellular metabolism, are of more significance in clinical considerations. For that reason, those symptoms will be treated briefly only as they assist in gaining an understanding of the general coordinative function of the endocrines.

Endocrines are frequently discussed in groups according to their glandular source. This approach also favors clinical and pathological considerations, for the dysfunction of a gland will generally result in its failure to produce a number of hormones in the proper amount. The set of symptoms which appears may actually result from the mutual action of more than one of the hormones, and the dysfunction of one gland in turn may have a decided effect on the secretory function of another.

In this chapter, the hormones will be discussed in groups according to the particular type of function with which they are involved. While this will place in groups hormones whose sources are far separated, it allows an emphasis on the basic role which they play in coordinating body functions.

SECRETORY CONTROL

Mention has already been made of gastrin, pancreozymin and cholecystokinin (page 95), all tissue hormones of the digestive tract.

Gastrin is produced in the stomach in response to the presence of food and brings about the secretion of pepsin, a protein-digesting enzyme, by the gastric glands. Hydrochloric acid is also produced by those glands. Its presence is essential for the proper pH at which pepsin will function. As the digestive mixtures are moved from the stomach into the intestine, the acid present stimulates the formation of two hormones by the intestinal mucosa. Pancreozymin is carried by the blood to the pancreas and causes secretion through a duct and into the intestine of the pancreatic juice which contains a mixture of digestive enzymes. The acid from the stomach is neutralized by the alkaline secretions, a condition essential for pancreatic digestion. Further assurance of a slightly alkaline condition in the intestine is furnished by the bile which is forced from the gall bladder as its walls contract under the influence of cholecystokinin. All of these mechanisms are essential for the normal digestion of food, and they are related in that their functions follow in a particular sequence. It should be noted that the relationship is unidirectional, for the appearance of gastrin sets into action a sequence of events eventually leading to intestinal digestion, but the latter neither increases nor decreases the function of the former. This is essential for the normal processes of digestion as food moves in one direction through the alimentary tract.

The anterior lobe of the pituitary gland (the *adenohypophysis*) produces at least six hormones, all but one of which influence secretions by another glandular structure. Because of its widespread influence over other endocrine glands, the adenohypophysis has been referred to as the master gland of the body. It is interesting to note, however, that the secretions of the glands controlled may in turn have some influence over the pituitary. It is through such mutual control that best assurance is furnished for the maintenance of a constant condition within the body.

The *thyrotrophic hormone* (TSH) is normally produced in such quantity that it stimulates the thyroid gland to secrete sufficient amounts of thyroxin into the blood stream for the regulation of oxidative and developmental metabolism. An excess of thyroxin in the blood will suppress the further liberation of TSH. This condition will result in less stimulation to produce thyroxin. Conversely, if the thyroxin level in the blood is low there is an increase in the formation of TSH and this results in greater thyroxin release. This type of reciprocal control is also seen in the instance of the *adrenocorticotrophic hormone* (ACTH) which stimulates the adrenal cortex to produce its hormones and in turn has its formation regulated by the level of those hormones in the blood.

The anterior pituitary also produces the *gonadotrophic hormones, follicle stimulating hormone* (FSH) and *luteinizing hormone* (LH). The specific responses to the presence of these hormones will be considered later. It is sufficient at this point of the discussion to indicate that FSH and LH stimulate the formation of sex hormones. The level of a sex hormone will in turn cause an increase or decrease in the amount or even determine the specific type of gonadotrophin produced. In the female FSH is produced early in the reproductive cycle and initiates a sequence of mutually controlling secretions in which estradiol, LH and progesterone appear in that order. The occurrence of each hormone in the proper sequence is essential for certain events of the reproductive cycle. In this instance, there are reciprocal controls, but they must follow in a particular order for the proper coordination of a body function.

The relations between the adenohypophysis and other glandular structures may be indicated as follows:

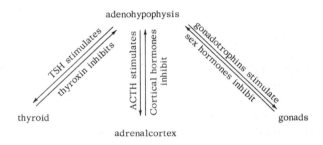

Prolactin stimulates milk secretion by the mammary gland. In order that it may have such effect the female sex hormones, estradiol and progesterone, must first have had the opportunity to stimulate proper development of the gland. This will have occurred previous to and during pregnancy as a result of early high levels of progesterone and later comparative predominance of estradiol in the blood. The placenta, through which nutrients are furnished to the developing fetus, also will have developed under the stimulating effect of high quantities of progesterone early in pregnancy. It serves as an endocrine gland, producing materials inhibitory to the release of prolactin. Late in pregnancy this inhibitory effect diminishes as does the progesterone level. This allows some prolactin to be released and to stimulate the final development of the mammary glands previous to their secretion. Following parturition, or birth the adenohypophysis is released from placental inhibition so prolactin is furnished in greater quantities, and the mammary glands are stimulated into normal secretion.

HOMEOSTASIS

Homeostasis is the maintenance of a constant but dynamic condition within the body. To some extent, the nervous system serves in such a capacity, especially as it controls the heart and circulatory system and the function of organs for digestion and excretion. The secretions of the endocrine glands also are involved, being especially suited for homeostatic control in that their action is more prolonged than is that of nervous stimulation. It is through the action of hormones that the fluids which bathe the body's cells are maintained constant in relation to ionic content, nutrients and other organic materials essential for the maintenance of life. Hormones also contribute to the regulation of a constant body temperature in birds and mammals.

Carbohydrates are the main energy source for all cells of the body. A constant level of metabolism will generally relate to the level at which carbohydrates are available, either from the fluid environment or from stored sources within cells. Most cells use carbohydrate in the form of glucose, which initially is made available from the intestine following digestion and absorption into the blood stream. Immediately following absorption the excess carbohydrate in the blood is converted enzymatically into glycogen (*glycogenesis*) to be stored in the liver and to a lesser degree in muscle tissue. During fasting the body's cells utilize glucose from the blood to the extent that levels would be drastically reduced were it not for other enzyme systems of the liver which reconvert the glycogen to glucose (*glycogenolysis*) so that it is liberated into the blood stream. Through such mechanisms the glucose level in mammalian blood is kept constant at about 100 mgm. per 100 ml. This furnishes a distinct advantage over lower forms, where greater variation occurs. Endocrines play a significant role in the control of a constantly available carbohydrate source.

Insulin is a polypeptide produced by clusters of cells in the pancreas called the *islets of Langerhans*. Its effect is to increase glycogenesis so that under normal conditions the muscles contain about one per cent and the liver as much as ten per cent glycogen. Glycogen in muscle is mainly for use by that tissue in its energy metabolism, but the liver serves as a depot for stored carbohydrates that may eventually be used by any of the body's tissues.

Insulin plays an important role immediately following food intake as absorbed glucose is converted into liver glycogen and stored for future use. In the event of insulin insufficiency, as in *diabetes mellitus*, liver glycogenesis does not occur. As a result, the accumulating excess of glucose in the blood is eventually lost from the body by way of the kidneys. Subsequently, the body tissues suffer from an inadequate energy source. Weakness follows and death may occur in serious cases. Insulin administration will offset the diabetic condition, but care must be taken for an overdose will result in fainting and death. This is due to the fact that the nervous tissue stores very little glycogen and is actually dependent on the blood stream for a constant glucose supply. Excessive liver glycogenesis may so reduce the blood level that a dangerous situation develops in relation to the brain.

Glucagon, another endocrine from the pancreas, is produced by the alpha cells of that organ in response to low levels of blood sugar. It causes liver glycogenolysis in an attempt to restore normal blood sugar levels. A proper balance of insulin and glucagon, or their altered liberation as the situation may demand, furnishes the means for regulation of sugar metabolism within the entire body.

Epinephrine, also causes liver glycogenolysis. In emergency situations such as fright or anger, nerve impulses from the hypothalamus cause the adrenal medulla to release epinephrine into the blood stream, and there follows an increase in blood sugar. The hormone causes the blood vessels to change in caliber so that blood is directed from the abdominal region out into the muscles with the result that more glucose and oxygen are made available. Since epinephrine increases the rate at which glucose is utilized in cellular metabolism, there exists a potential for increased muscle power, a desirable condition for meeting the emergency situation. By adding the effect of epinephrine to those of insulin and glucagon, the body is furnished additional means for regulating metabolism and adjusting the internal environment.

The control of body temperature is another homeostatic mechanism. The nervous system is involved in that it regulates the flow of blood through vessels in the skin and also stimulates the sweat glands into secretion. Nerve impulses also are carried to certain endocrine glands, stimulating them to release their secretions which may in turn contribute to the control of body temperature. This homeostatic mechanism furnishes an excellent example of the extent to which nervous and hormonal factors may be interrelated. In the instance of exposure to cold, another type of emergency situation, the stimulation of Krause end bulbs results in the conduction of impulses to the hypothalamus. From there they are relayed to the appropriate effectors to complete a reflex adjustment to meet the emergency. Among the effector organs stimulated are the adrenal and thyroid glands.

The manner of epinephrine involvement has already been mentioned, for the accelerated oxidative processes will increase heat production. The effect is seen within a short time, but the rapid destruction of epinephrine results in its relatively brief duration. Thyroxin is more slowly destroyed, and its effect may persist for hours after its release. It will be recalled that thyroxin uncouples phosphorylation so that oxidation occurs more rapidly. Furthermore, the energy of the chemical reactions, instead of being stored in ATP, is lost as heat. Such inefficiency would in this instance be desirable in meeting the immediate need of the body.

That the thyroid gland plays an important role in regulating body temperature is given further proof in situations resulting from its dysfunction. Persons who suffer from thyroid deficiency show reduced total metabolism as indicated by the lower rate of oxygen consumption. As a rule, body temperature also is decreased. Treatment of this condition consists of the administration of thyroid extracts or pure thyroxin, and there ensues an increased oxidative metabolism in direct relation to the amount of material given. It is not surprising that experimental administration of thyroxin to most forms of animal life results in increased respiration, since the function is directed toward enzymatic actions more or less the same in all cells.

The proper adjustment of ionic concentrations in body fluids is extremely important for the optimum function of cells, tissues and organs. The heart, for example, is strongly influenced by monovalent and divalent cations, the former slowing and the latter increasing its rhythmic contractions. The proper balance of calcium and magnesium is essential for muscle contraction, and an excess of magnesium has a general anesthetic effect.

Parathormone is essential in that it controls the balance of calcium in the blood and skeletal structures. Experimental removal of the parathyroid glands results in muscular twitching, prostration and eventually death. Animals so treated show considerable reduction in blood calcium levels. Administration of the hormone will temporarily raise blood calcium to normal, apparently as the material is mobilized from bone. It is not known exactly how this may be effected, but the hormone probably regulates phosphorylation reactions through which the calcium is reversibly converted to soluble or insoluble products.

The kidney is the most important organ of the body for the maintenance of sodium and potassium balance. In the first phase of urine formation water and its dissolved salts are filtered from the blood stream to move into the renal tubules. A second phase involves the active reabsorption of materials essential to the body, back into the blood stream before the urine passes from the kidney. If it were not for this reabsorption considerable loss of salts would result. Much of the reabsorption is controlled by hormones from the adrenal cortex referred to as the *mineralocorticoids*. Deoxycorticosterone is an example of such compounds. Under its influence, the renal tubule cells are stimulated to reabsorb sodium and chloride back into the blood, while at the same time the rate at which potassium is reabsorbed is decreased, resulting in its greater excretion. In the absence of mineralocorticoids there is such a loss of body sodium that serious departures from the normal homeostatic condition may cause death. It follows, of course, that the proper function of the adenohypophysis through its secretion of ACTH would be essential for this phase of homeostatic mechanisms. It would be difficult to explain a failure in this mechanism on the basis of improper control by a single gland or hormone.

The *posterior pituitary gland* (*neurohypophysis*) influences homeostasis by regulation of water balance. During the second reabsorptive phase of urine formation, much of the water which had filtered from the blood into the renal tubules is returned by active process. This occurs under the influence of an *antidiuretic principle* or the combined effects of other neurohypophyseal factors. *Diabetes insipidus*, a condition of hormonal deficiency, results in severe water loss from the body—up to ten times the normal 1.5 liters per day—due to failure of its reabsorption.

GROWTH AND DIFFERENTIATION

Many factors will contribute to the total growth effect, among them the availability of foods, their proper digestion and absorption and influence of genetic factors over the initial potential of the animal to attain a certain size within the allowances for species variation. Genetic factors also influence the processes which account for differentiation. Hormones control growth and differentiation, in part perhaps, through the effect they have on enzymatic reactions involving amino acids, the building blocks for protein and protoplasm. It is unlikely that hormonal stimulation of growth may be explained in such a simple and direct manner, but the gross effects are easily identified.

Growth in the vertebrates is mainly under the control of somatotrophin (STH) from the adenohypophysis. Individuals suffering from this hormone's deficiency, or animals from which the gland has been removed for experimental purposes, fail to attain normal adult size. Body proportions are normal however, so there is 'a tendency to develop structural and functional aspects of maturity even in the absence of increase in size. The growth promoting effect of STH is exerted in the areas of enlargement and elongation of skeletal structures. If an excess of STH is present in the young individual a condition of *gigantism* results. Excessive growth occurs especially in the long bones of the extremities. If the gland should function normally until adulthood, at which time the growth centers of the long bones have become solidly calcified so that further elongation may not occur, an excessive production of STH will then cause enlargement of the membranous bones of the skull with its resulting enlargement. STH also affects growth of skeletal muscle tissue, resulting in its enlargement and greater strength. A disadvantage in gigantism is seen in the greater body size which places such a strain on the heart, in pumping blood greater distances through the circulatory system, that longivity may be diminished.

The thyroid gland also is important in early growth and development, and thyroid deficiency in the young animal results in a type of dwarfism, known as *cretinism*. There is a notable difference in the cretin dwarf, resulting from thyroid deficiency and the pituitary dwarf, for in the former there is a tendency to retain infantile characteristics. The limbs fail to elongate as they should and in extreme situations there is a failure in normal mental development. Such situations, if detected early and properly treated by the administration of thyroxin, may be dramatically corrected so normal physical and mental growth will occur.

The true nature of thyroxin's effect may be demonstrated in the maturing frog. During metamorphosis the tadpole undergoes changes in external body form and internal organ systems in becoming an adult. The removal of the thyroid glands from an early tadpole will prevent the occurrence of metamorphosis with the result that growth continues in the formation of a giant tadpole, but differentiation never occurs. If thyroxin is added to water containing tadpoles they are caused to undergo rapid metamorphosis, so processes of differentiation normally taking many weeks will be completed in a fraction of that time. Such stimulation may result in the formation of pygmy frogs. If an excess of thyroxin is added metamorphosis may be completed in a few days, but death usually results from the excessive stimulation of oxidative metabolism and failure to furnish energy in the normal manner through ATP production. Some amphibians are neotenous; that is, they retain to some degree their immature form. The larval form of the salamander, ambystoma (commonly called axolotl), possesses external gills which persist even in the adult. Thyroxin administration will cause such adults to shed the gills and develop lungs.

Normal vertebrate growth and development is seen to depend on the proper balance of pituitary and thyroid control. A complex control exists over the process of growth and differentiation as they occur in insect molting. Insect development with its wide variations during progression from egg to larva, pupa and adult furnishes an excellent opportunity to investigate hormonal control over these processes.

Some of the earlier work of note was accomplished by the Englishman, V. B. Wigglesworth on the bloodsucking tropical bug, *Rhodnius*. Larval molts occur in five nymphal stages, each of which is larger than the last and more closely resembles the adult. Feeding after each molt acts as the stimulus to set in action a series of events leading to the next. While the time required between molts may vary, it is constant for a given nymphal stage. Furthermore, the processes essential for molting, if having progressed sufficiently past a critical time, will continue the molt regardless of subsequent treatment. This may be demonstrated by removal of the head before the critical time has elapsed, thus preventing the molt; however, if decapitation is accomplished after the critical time, the molt will still occur. While the brain seemed important for initiation of the molting processes, it was shown that their completion depended on factors in the blood. If two decapitated animals were joined by a tiny capillary tube so that their bloods might be exchanged, it was observed that such telobiosis of an animal decapitated before the critical time with one decapitated afterward would result in the molting of both.

The involvement of more than a single factor was shown by telobiosis of late-decapitated first with an early-decapitated fifth nymphal stage. Following such union the first stage molted to become a small adult, while the fifth molted to become a normal adult. In a combination involving a late-decapitated first-stage nymph with an early-decapitated fifth stage, the former molts normally, while the latter instead of becoming an adult molts again to form a sixth and larger nymphal stage. This indicates the presence of two types of hormonal factors; one of these induces molting and differentiation, while the other allows the molt to occur but prevents form differentiation.

Other interesting observations have been made by Carroll Williams on the developing stages of the cecropia moth. Cecropia varies from Rhodnius in that during metamorphosis it forms a pupal stage prior to the last and dramatic molt at which time its form changes abruptly to the winged adult. The last molt will not occur unless the pupa is chilled for several weeks at about 5°C. and then warmed to normal temperature. Pupa so treated may be sectioned, the cut ends sealed and observed continuously for molting. A section between the thorax and abdomen results in an anterior half which molts on chilling, but the abdomen does not. Sectioning of a pupa above the thorax and subsequent chilling of the halves prevents molting; however, a molt may be induced by transplantation of the brain from a chilled pupa into the posterior portion. Such does not occur if the transplant is made into a posterior portion consisting only of abdomen. Such observations demonstrate the significance of control by a thoracic factor as well as by some material from the brain.

As a result of these and other studies the processes of molting, which involve both growth and differentiation, may be represented as following the order of (1) stimulation, (2) brain activation of (3) glands in the head region, (4) hormonal activation of (5) thoracic glands to release the (6) molting hormone and finally (7) the occurrence of the molt.

The stimulus may be the availability of nutrients or a temperature change, normally occurring with the seasons or simulated in the laboratory by chilling. In the pupa of cecropia brain activity is low previous to chilling, but there follows an increase in ACh and cholinesterase activity and development of measurable action potentials. Concurrently, secretions from the supraesophageal ganglion are transmitted via nerves to the *corpora cardiaca,* small glandular structures lying near the brain. The *corpora cardiaca* are the source of a hormone which is carried in the blood to the thoracic region, there to stimulate the formation of the *molting hormone.*

The thoracic gland is thought to be the source of the molting hormone, *ecdyson.* That material is released into the blood stream and carried to the cuticular region where it stimulates epithelial mitosis essential for growth and differentiation and causes the formation of the new cuticle following the molt. Ecdyson which has been isolated from thoracic glands of one insect is effective in inducing a molt when introduced into other species.

The observation that telobiosis of an earlier Rhodnius nymph with a final nymphal stage will prevent the differentiation to an adult first suggested the presence of a *juvenile hormone.* This hormone is produced by the *corpora allata,* another glandular structure in the region of the brain. It prevents the epithelial processes of differentiation which normally result in adult formation but does not interfere with the molt itself. Juvenile hormone is not produced during those molts leading to the adult. It has been isolated from insect tissue and on being introduced into pupal moths prevents the final molt from forming the adult, so another and larger pupal stage results. The general interaction of these various structures and hormones is shown by the chart on the following page.

It would seem that special chemical factors from mammalian cells and from the lowest of the invertebrates also may be involved in developmental differentiation. Cells from kidney tissue that has been dis-

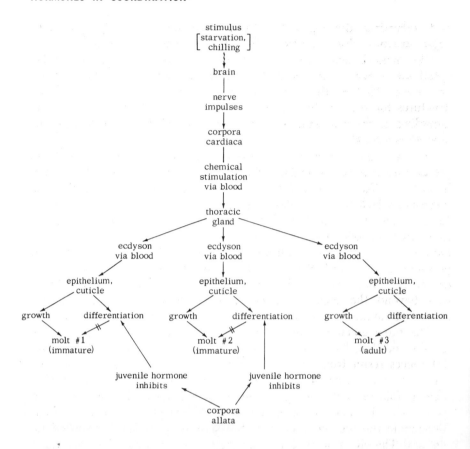

rupted for culture *in vitro* will in time accumulate on the bottom of the culture vessel in circular patterns suggestive of cross sections of kidney tubules. If a sponge is forced through a cloth sieve so that only single cells or fragments of a few cells are present, these will in a period of a few hours move together to form aggregates as though regenerating a new sponge. In the slime mold, Physarium, amoeboid cells aggregate about other particular types previous to fusion and formation of the plasmodium, a multinuclear cytoplasmic sheet. The nature of the stimuli causing these various types of aggregations and differentiations is not known.

REPRODUCTION AND SEXUAL DIFFERENTIATION

Reproduction in the metazoa involves a great variety of processes including the self-replication of nucleic acid in chromosome duplication, the formation and union of ovum and spermatozoan in fertilization and embryonic development with differentiation in body form and organ structure characteristic of the sex and in some instances essential for the reproductive process itself. Genetic control is generally the initial factor for determining the sex of the individual. The *primary sex organs;* that is, the testes and ovaries and the associated tubule structures for the conduction of the ova or spermatozoa, will develop according to the chromosomal composition which is established at the time of fertilization.

As the animal approaches sexual maturity development of the primary sex organs is stimulated by the gonadotrophins from the adenohypophysis. The testes and ovaries in turn produce their specific sex hormones which cause the development of *secondary sex characteristics.* In the male the formation of gonadotrophins and sex hormones continues more or less constant throughout life. In the female, however, the hormones are produced at different times in cyclic recurrence, and the presence of one will have an effect on the production and action of others which follow. The function of the reproductive structures goes beyond the purpose of our present discussion concerning the major coordinating actions of the various endocrines.

The same gonadotrophins are produced in both the male and the female, and their basic functions are similar in both sexes. The apparent differences result from the cells, which are the targets of their action, and since these cells have different chromosomal composition in the sexes it follows that their potential for action and differentiation will vary. That the nomenclature of the gonadotrophins relates to their function in the female is because the actions were first recognized in that sex. The chemical nature of this group of hormones does not vary, nor does their influence, on male or female primary sex organs.

Follicle stimulating hormone (FSH) affects those regions of the testes and ovaries concerned with the formation of spermatozoa and ova, respectively. In either instance, cells are caused to undergo a series of meiotic divisions resulting in the final formation of haploid reproductive cells. In the testes this occurs within the seminiferous tubules. The ovum develops within the *Graafian follicle* in the cortical portion of the ovary. Actually, FSH is concerned mainly with the initial development of the ovum, and another gonadotrophin predominates later in the reproductive cycle, directing further development until the mature follicle ruptures to release the ovum in ovulation. FSH also stimulates the formation of follicular hormone, estradiol, the function of which will be considered later.

The second of the gonadotrophins is the luteinizing hormone (LH). LH is produced during the female reproductive cycle in response to rising estradiol concentration in the blood, that material having been formed in the follicle in response to initial FSH stimulation. Under the influence of LH the follicle reaches maturity and ovulation occurs. There follows a cellular proliferation into the vacated follicle with the formation of the *corpus luteum.* That structure is the source of the luteal hormone, progesterone. Its presence in the blood supresses further formation of FSH. Progesterone concentrations diminish toward the end of the female reproductive cycle, at which time FSH is again released, and the cycle is repeated. These events are repeated during the reproductive life of the female. As one of the processes of aging the amount of hormonal secretion diminishes with resulting discontinuation of the reproductive cycle.

In the male LH stimulates the interstitial cells of the testes to produce the male sex hormone. Previous designation of the hormone as ICSH was an effort to recognize a separate hormone in the male. Present general concurrence holds that LH and ICSH are the same hormone, and the latter designation is merely an attempt to identify the specific function in the male. Actually, the basic function is the same in both sexes, that is, the stimulation of sex hormone formation.

The most important of the *sex hormones* are estradiol and progesterone in the female and testosterone in the male. They influence the development of such secondary sex characteristics as musculature and skeletal structure, body hair, depth of voice, external genitalia and the mammary glands. In the lower forms of life such characteristics also include feather coloration, the comb of the fowl, migratory habits and nest building in birds and coloration in certain fishes.

Because the level of gonadotrophins remains approximately constant throughout reproductive life in the male, it follows that the level of sex hormone and reproduction capacity will remain unchanged. In the female, however, the cyclic changes in hormonal production result in repeated ovulation. Estradiol and progesterone, each in its turn, effect changes of the uterine structure, first for reception of the fertilized ovum and later for protection and nutrition of the newly developing individual.

If pregnancy occurs the *corpus luteum* persists and continues to produce progesterone. That hormone supresses a return of the pituitary to the formation of FSH so that the reproductive cycle is temporarily discontinued. Progesterone also has a stimulatory effect on the development of the *placenta,* that structure within which the new individual develops. The placenta in turn produces more progesterone and a variety of other materials which contribute to the continuation of conditions most favorable for pregnancy. Late in pregnancy placental secretions gradually diminish, and this may relate indirectly to the initiation of the birth process or parturition. *Oxytocin* from the *posterior pituitary* (neurohypophysis) will cause strong contractions of the uterus late in pregnancy.

The development and normal secretion of the mammary glands is influenced by the female sex hormones as well as prolactin from the adenohypophysis. Prolactin produced in the male will be without effect on mammary gland development since the proper sex hormones are lacking. The initiation of mammary gland secretion following parturition is related to the reduction in blood placental hormones so they no longer inhibit release of prolactin by the adenohypophysis.

Although proof is lacking for the occurrence of gonadotrophins and sex hormones in the invertebrates, it seems likely that some type of chemical control exists. The corpora allata of insects is thought to control egg production, and there is evidence for reciprocal control between that structure and the ovaries much in the same manner as between the pituitary and the corpus luteum. Environmental conditions such as light and temperature influence reproductive function in the crustacea and echinoderms, but the possible involvement of chemical coordinators remains to be established.

Conjugation in the ciliates and zygote formation in the phytoflagellates represent sexual reproduction in the simplest forms of animal life. Attempts have been made to explain the initiation of conjugation on the basis of nutrient depletion or accumulation of extracellular and intracellular wastes, but none of these explanations is generally accepted. Ciliate conjugation may be induced by the addition of certain ions to the water, but such a stimulation seems not directly comparable to a hormonal effect. There is evidence that mating types of phytoflagellates are mutually attracted by chemical agents of the flagella, for this is the region of initial attachment previous to cellular fusion. The production of flagellar attractants is related to photosynthetic activity, indicating a close coordination of biochemical activities. The relations of chemical coordinators in these protozoan forms to their total metabolic activity furnish an interesting challenge for investigation into animal control mechanisms at the cellular level.

. . . .

It is not inferred that the answers to these problems of unicellular coordination will be immediately forthcoming; neither should it be anticipated that their eventual solution will be applicable in a predictable degree to coordinating mechanisms in metazoan forms. Some of the essential information for the solution of protozoan problems will undoubtedly come from research on higher forms. It is in the appreciation of possible common factors in all cellular metabolism and through the appropriate application of present information in the studies which must follow that today's questions will become tomorrow's knowledge and lead in turn to further inquiry.

ADDITIONAL READING

BARRINGTON, E. J. W., *Hormones and Evolution,* London: English Universities Press, 1964, pp. 1-43.

JENKIN, PENELOPE M., *Animal Hormones—A Comparative Survey,* New York: Pergamon Press, Inc., pp. 167-259.

VANDERKLOOT, WILLIAM G., "Insect Metamorphosis and its Endocrine Control," *American Zoologist* 1:3-9, 1961.

Index

591.1
Mcc

McCashland, Benjamin W
    Animal coordinating
    mechanisms.

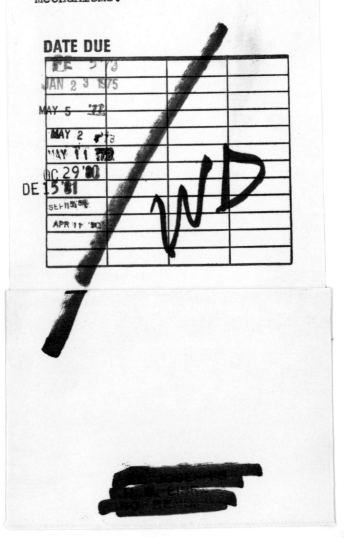